COMPREHENSION QUARTERLY

CQ

4

ISSUE A: Synthesizing

How Sweet It Is!

How Sweet It Is!

THINK ABOUT: Synthesizing

A4

NONFICTION
Ice-Cream Time!
Tantalize your taste buds with ice-cream tidbits.

A11

FICTION
Hooked on Worms
Find out about Miranda and her worm tea.

FICTION
Hank and Gretchen
Follow them into the Lost Forest.

A19

A24

NONFICTION
Wildlife Watching
Swim with manatees, look for moose, and track wolves.

SYNTHESIZING

The Power of Smell

Tamika is writing a paraphrase of an article on the sense of smell for science class. Here is how the article begins.

Animals' lives are ruled by smells and other chemical signals. They use scents to find food and recognize trails, territory, relatives, and mates. For example, chemical signals tell ants and some other insects what to do and how to behave every minute of the day.

Human beings usually use their eyes and ears for information instead of using the sense of smell. People are considered rude if they even mention some smells— other people's body odors, for example. Yet a recent study showed that some people love the smell of their grandmothers above all other odors. Also, mothers can recognize their newborn babies by smell, and babies recognize their mother's odor in return. Have you ever caught a whiff of a scent and been transported instantly to another time and place? If so, you know the power of smell.

Tamika knows that a paraphrase is a kind of restatement. She needs to tell the author's important ideas in her own words. Often, a paraphrase will be simpler and slightly shorter than the original. Tamika **synthesized** as she read the article by taking notes to remember the important information. Then she organized and reworded her notes into a paragraph.

SMELL

animals: find food, trails, chemical signals, ants

people: use eyes and ears, not nose
mothers and babies know each other
smells help you remember

Smells are very important to animals. They use smells to find food, trails, and other things they need to survive. Chemical signals tell ants what to do every day. People use their eyes and ears more than their noses. But smells are important to people, too. For example, mothers and babies know each other by smell. Also, smells can help people remember times and places.

ICE-CREAM TIME!

by **Susan Meyers**

Who likes ice cream? Just about everyone! Strawberry, vanilla, or chocolate chip, eaten from a cup or a cone—it's America's favorite treat. In fact, people in the United States eat more ice cream than anyone else in the world—nearly 1.5 billion gallons a year!

In the early days, ice cream was eaten plain, out of a bowl, and with a spoon. But it wasn't long before people got creative. Here's how a number of popular ice-cream treats were invented.

Ice-Cream Sodas

In the early 1870s, a favorite soda fountain drink was made by pouring cream into flavored soda water. One day in 1874, Robert Green, a Philadelphia soda fountain operator, ran out of cream. He thought he would melt some ice cream to use instead, but with hungry customers waiting, he decided to try something new. Boldly, he dropped a scoop of ice cream into soda water and served it up. His customers loved it! Green's sales skyrocketed. Inspired by his success, he went on to make a fortune in the soda fountain business.

Other people claimed to have invented the ice-cream soda, too. Perhaps they did. It's hard to say who was first, but one thing's certain—the ice-cream soda was an idea whose time had come!

No one knows who invented ice cream. The ancient Chinese ate a frozen dessert made from horsemilk, rice, and flour. The Roman emperor, Nero, is said to have served sweet fruit ices made from snow his slaves gathered in the mountains. That wasn't ice cream as we know it, either. The first real ice cream was probably made in Italy in the seventeenth century. From there it traveled to France and England. By the mid-eighteenth century, ice cream had made its way to the American colonies.

What do you know so far about where ice cream came from?

George Washington, the first president of the United States, liked ice cream and served it at his dinner parties—so did Thomas Jefferson, the third president, and James Madison, the fourth. Madison's wife Dolley was famous for entertaining. Her dessert table at the White House often included magnificent silver platters piled high with ice cream and strawberries.

Ice-Cream Sundaes

In the 1880s, church-goers in Evanston, Illinois, were upset about people hanging out in soda fountains on Sunday. They passed a local law prohibiting the sale of ice-cream sodas on that day. Soda fountain operators got around the law by creating a new treat—a dish of ice cream with chocolate or fruit syrup poured over it. The new creation came to be called a Sunday, since that's when it was served. Later on the spelling was changed, and sundaes were served every day of the week.

Like the ice-cream soda, the ice-cream sundae may well have been created in more than one place. No matter how it happened, there's no doubt that having a sundae soon became a favorite way to splurge. Whether hot fudge, caramel, or strawberry, the fantabulous ice-cream sundae was a megahit!

In those days, ice for freezing ice cream was hard to come by. It had to be cut from frozen lakes during the winter, then packed in sawdust and stored in ice houses with thick walls for use during the rest of the year.

Preparing the ice cream wasn't easy, either. It was a two-person job that took several hours. First, a large pot was filled with crushed ice and salt. The salt melted the ice. A smaller pot filled with a mixture of milk, cream, sugar, and flavoring was nested inside the larger pot. Now the real work began. As one person stirred the ice-cream mixture, the other shook the pot. Keeping everything moving was the key to success. If the mixture rested too long against the sides of the pot, large ice crystals would form. Instead of being smooth and creamy, the ice cream would be full of hard lumps!

With so much work involved, it's not surprising that ice cream was a treat reserved for wealthy people who could afford servants to make it. Not until the 1840s did ice cream become available to ordinary people. It was all due to an ingenious machine invented by a Philadelphia woman named Nancy Johnson.

What did you learn about making ice cream 100 years ago?

Ice Cream for Everyone!

Not much is known about Nancy Johnson herself, but the hand-cranked ice-cream freezer that she designed was patented in 1848. It revolutionized ice-cream making in America.

The Johnson Patent Ice-Cream Freezer had a metal pail with a removable lid that sat inside a wooden bucket. The ice-cream mixture went into the pail. Crushed ice and salt went into the space between the pail and the bucket. A hand crank, extending through the lid, turned an S-shaped paddle inside the pail. The paddle, or dasher, scraped ice crystals from the sides of the pail and kept the mixture constantly moving so that it froze into smooth and creamy ice cream.

Today's hand-cranked ice-cream freezers work just like Nancy Johnson's original did.

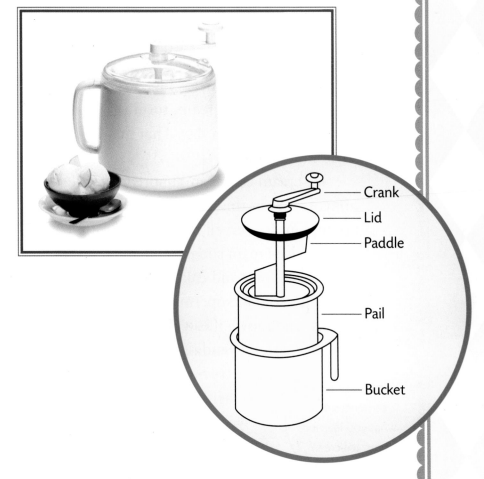

- Crank
- Lid
- Paddle
- Pail
- Bucket

Ice-Cream Cones

In 1904, a World's Fair was held in St. Louis. Vendors sold all kinds of treats, including ice cream and a type of Middle-Eastern waffle called *zalabia*. One hot day, an ice-cream seller ran out of dishes. The waffle vendor next door came to his rescue. He rolled a freshly made *zalabia* into a cone, instantly creating an edible container for ice cream. The idea caught on quickly. Soon people all over America were eating their ice cream from cones.

Ice-Cream Bars

One day in 1919, a boy came into a small ice-cream and candy store in Onawa, Iowa. He had money in his pocket but couldn't decide how to spend it. Should he buy ice cream or a chocolate bar? The boy's dilemma gave Christian Nelson, the owner of the store, an idea. Why not meld the boy's favorite treats into a chocolate-covered ice-cream bar? He experimented for months and finally figured out how to do it. He had invented the ice-cream bar.

Top 10
Ice Cream Flavors

1 Vanilla

2 Chocolate

3 Neapolitan

4 Butter Pecan

5 Cookies 'N' Cream

6 Strawberry

7 Chocolate Chip

8 Mint Chocolate Chip

9 Vanilla/Chocolate

10 Marble Fudge

Flavors That Never Made the Top 10

- Prune
- Licorice
- Pumpernickel Rye Bread
- Sea Urchin
- Chile-con-carne
- Ketchup
- Sweet Pickle
- Asparagus

People loved the new machine. It was inexpensive enough for a middle-class family to buy. It made ice cream in less time and with far less effort than the old method. Best of all, it was fun! Ice-cream making became a part of family parties and picnics. Everyone, including children, took a turn at the crank and got to enjoy delicious homemade ice cream.

Why did people like this ice-cream machine?

People still make ice cream at home, but today most ice cream is made in factories. Huge machines mix and freeze the ice cream, turning out as much as 60,000 gallons a day. That's enough to fill 168 million cones!

Ice cream comes in hundreds of different flavors—everything from bubble gum to pumpkin. It's served in dozens of different ways—ice-cream sodas and sundaes, shakes and malts, pies and cakes, sandwiches and bars. It's sold at supermarkets, amusement parks, and movie theaters, and from ice-cream parlors, vending machines, and ice-cream trucks. You can be sure that anywhere you live, at any time of the year, ice cream is always near!

In one or two sentences, tell what you learned about ice cream.

Flavor Favorites

Survey your class to find out which flavor of ice cream is everyone's favorite. Display your findings on a bar graph. How many times more popular is the most popular flavor than the least popular flavor?

More Than Yummy

Here is a challenge: express the experience of eating ice cream in words. Think of everything you know and feel about ice cream. Sum up your thoughts in a T-chart, a word web, or another graphic organizer. Then use the ideas on the graphic organizer to create a mouth-watering ice-cream poem.

Not Everyone Screams for Ice Cream!

Surely, somebody in the world hates ice cream! What if that person were you? Write a short essay explaining why you think ice cream is a terrible food. Come up with as many reasons as you can about why people should never, ever eat ice cream.

Every Body EATS

Sure, everybody eats, but they don't eat the same foods and they also disagree about table manners. What's displeasing and uninviting to one person might be sweet and tempting to another. That goes for animals, too.

Fierce Frogs

Not all frogs are as harmless as they look. Argentina's ornate horned frog is an occasional cannibal. It eats just about anything its sticky tongue can pull into its gaping mouth—including other frogs.

Go to Sleep: I'm Hungry

Vampire bats of South America lap blood from sleeping prey. They make tiny cuts with their razor-sharp teeth and lap their victims' blood. Luckily the bats are tiny— about the size of a mouse—and the prey rarely becomes disabled or even wakes up. These tiny creatures are huge eaters; they lap their weight (about an ounce) in blood each night.

Tune In

The TV roach, or *Supella supellectilium,* likes to munch—you guessed it— televisions. Not the sets themselves, just the insulation, glue, and other assorted parts.

Seconds

The great horned owl enjoys a meal of rodents and other small animals, and it eats the same meal twice. About seven hours after dining, the owl regurgitates, or throws up, round pellets that contain the animals' bones and fur. Then the owl eats the pellets.

Hooked on Worms

by Katacha Diaz

Miranda has worms under the kitchen sink. But that's not a problem. She put the red wigglers there, and it's okay with her parents, too!

It all started a few months ago after a class trip to Treasures from the Earth Farm. The farm raises thousands and thousands of red wigglers and sells them by the pound. Red wigglers, the farm owner explained, are the ultimate recyclers because they love to eat kitchen scraps. And their favorite scraps, Mrs. Ortega said, are crushed eggshells, fruit and vegetable trimmings, rice, pasta, tea bags, coffee grounds and filters, and even used paper towels!

What are three things red wigglers like to eat?

Believe it or not, Mrs. Ortega explained, red wigglers need shelter, water, and food to survive, just like humans. And they are creatures of comfort, too. Worms like a cozy home, especially one with some soft bedding to curl up in. And the perfect bedding comes from old newspapers torn into thin strips. But one must make sure the worms have plenty to eat, because unlike humans, the red wigglers will gobble up the bedding if there's nothing else for them to eat.

But what came as a bigger surprise to Miranda and her classmates was when Mrs. Jones, their teacher, told them that people use the castings, or worm waste, as a fertilizer. That's right! People add castings to the soil or when they water their houseplants and outdoor gardens! The dark brown castings, Mrs. Jones explained, are very high in nitrogen and smell like coffee grounds. And, more importantly, the castings also have nutrients that help plants ward off insects and other predators.

On her way home from school that afternoon Miranda had an idea, so she decided to bike over to the hardware store. She walked up to the customer service desk. "Mrs. Jensen," Miranda asked slowly, "can you help me find a small plastic storage bin and minirake? I have a guesstimate for an idea and need to get some info."

"Follow me," said Mrs. Jensen, leading Miranda down several aisles. "Is this what you're looking for?"

"Yes, thank you," Miranda said. She jotted down the information and prices in her notebook.

> In your own words, tell why worm castings are important.

The weeks passed quickly for Miranda. She was busy doing extra chores around the house and babysitting to supplement her weekly allowance. She needed the extra money to make her business dream come true, but she had to be patient and work hard.

Pretty soon Miranda had all the money she needed to start her business. She rode her bike over to the hardware store where she bought the plastic bin and small hand rake. "Good luck with your business venture, Miranda!" Mrs. Jensen said. She handed Miranda the bin and the rake.

Miranda was very excited and couldn't wait to get home and get started. She'd been saving old newspapers for weeks now, and she had torn these into strips just like she'd seen Mrs. Ortega doing at Treasures from the Earth Farm. Miranda quickly filled the bin with the newspaper strips and poured water on them until they felt like a damp sponge. Miranda carefully drained the excess water because she didn't want her wigglers to drown. Now she was ready to go to the farm and get her supply of red wigglers.

Miranda's parents drove her out to Treasures from the Earth Farm where she bought half a pound, or 500, of the small red wigglers from Mrs. Ortega. "Welcome to the Squiggle Motel," Miranda said, as she put the worms inside the brand new bin.

Synthesize what you've read so far and think of five words to describe the red wigglers.

At first some of the wigglers wanted to escape, just like Mrs. Ortega had told her they would! But Miranda remembered what to do if this should happen, so she found a good sunny spot by the kitchen window and put the bin there for a few days. Soon the wigglers settled down and were busy eating the gourmet kitchen scraps Miranda buried in the bedding for them.

The time finally came to find a permanent home for the wigglers. Miranda decided to put the bin under the kitchen sink. That's the

perfect spot, she thought, because red wigglers are sensitive to light. Also, she could check on them daily, sprinkle water in the bin to make sure their bedding was moist, and make sure they had their favorite gourmet food treats to eat.

"Want to see my worm bin, Sunshine?" Miranda asked her older sister.

"Yuck!" screamed Sunshine. "Get those creepy, slimy, gross things out of here, Miranda!"

"They're not hurting you," Miranda said with a smile, "and besides, Mom and Dad said it's OK for me to keep my wigglers here in the kitchen."

"You're really weird," Sunshine chortled. "I don't know anyone who keeps worms as pets!"

Miranda ignored Sunshine's remark and grabbed a handful of the red wigglers for closer inspection. The rest of the wigglers dived into the damp newspaper strips to escape the light. "Mom's fixing scrambled eggs for brunch this morning. I hope you're very hungry because there will be lots and lots of eggshells, cukes, apple cores, melon rinds, and banana peels for you to eat!"

A few weeks later Miranda stopped feeding the wigglers and waited. Several days later she removed the bin cover and found the red wigglers had indeed been very busy. The bin was now full of worm waste!

Miranda took the bin outside to clean it. Using the small rake, she carefully moved the red wigglers to one side and put clean, damp newspaper strips and kitchen scraps on the other side. Pretty soon the wigglers crawled over each other and headed to the food. They were famished! The worms began to gobble up their favorite kitchen scraps while Miranda removed the castings. Now it was tea-making time!

> What have you learned so far about raising worms?

Miranda measured a cup of the wiggler castings and dropped them in an old teakettle her mother had given her. Then she added two quarts of water and mixed it. Miranda carefully poured small amounts of the mixture into recycled jars. Then she put a label on each jar and wrote:

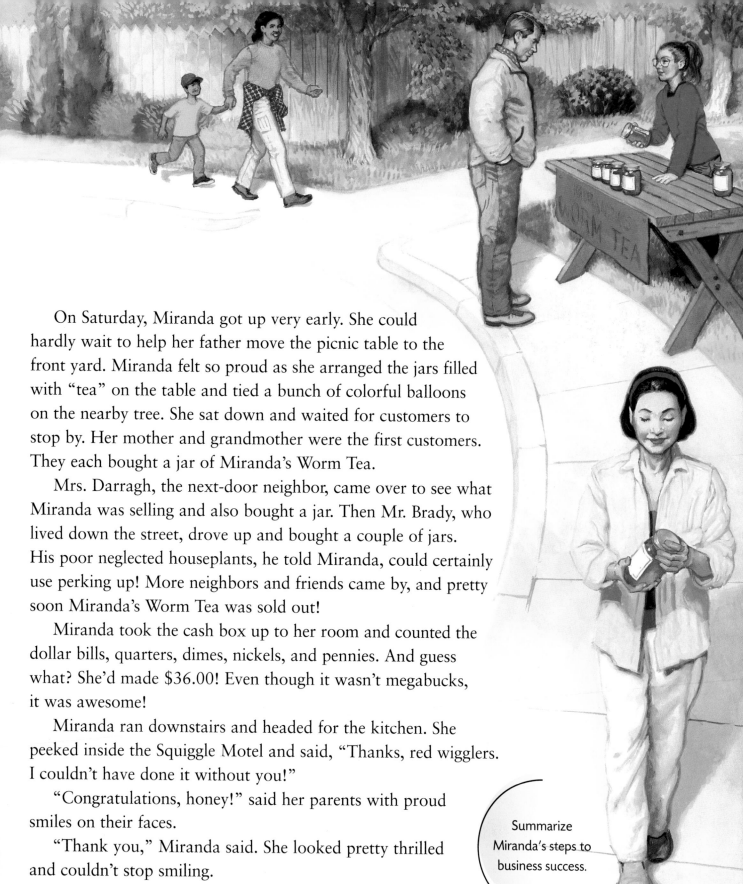

On Saturday, Miranda got up very early. She could hardly wait to help her father move the picnic table to the front yard. Miranda felt so proud as she arranged the jars filled with "tea" on the table and tied a bunch of colorful balloons on the nearby tree. She sat down and waited for customers to stop by. Her mother and grandmother were the first customers. They each bought a jar of Miranda's Worm Tea.

Mrs. Darragh, the next-door neighbor, came over to see what Miranda was selling and also bought a jar. Then Mr. Brady, who lived down the street, drove up and bought a couple of jars. His poor neglected houseplants, he told Miranda, could certainly use perking up! More neighbors and friends came by, and pretty soon Miranda's Worm Tea was sold out!

Miranda took the cash box up to her room and counted the dollar bills, quarters, dimes, nickels, and pennies. And guess what? She'd made $36.00! Even though it wasn't megabucks, it was awesome!

Miranda ran downstairs and headed for the kitchen. She peeked inside the Squiggle Motel and said, "Thanks, red wigglers. I couldn't have done it without you!"

"Congratulations, honey!" said her parents with proud smiles on their faces.

"Thank you," Miranda said. She looked pretty thrilled and couldn't stop smiling.

It took lots of hard work, but Miranda's Worm Tea was a sweet success. Maybe now, Miranda thought, Sunshine will feel differently about my red wigglers. And who knows, Sunshine may get hooked on worms and start her own tea business, too! ◉

Summarize Miranda's steps to business success.

Stop and Respond

You're in Business!

Design an advertisement for Miranda's business. Use a word web to help you organize your ideas. Be sure to include the benefits of worm tea. Use your ideas along with eye-catching illustrations to make your ad.

How to Make Worm Tea

Do you remember all the steps Miranda went through to make worm tea? Make a step chart and write the tea-making steps in the proper order on it. When you're through, compare your chart to a classmate's. Did you include all the steps? Check the story if you are not sure.

Wiggler Squiggles

Worms are easy to draw, and who says they don't have personalities! Draw the comic-strip adventures of a bunch of worms. Perhaps they are the worms Miranda is raising to make worm tea, or they may be different worms who have different adventures. Don't forget to title your comic strip and sign your name.

Pets
and Their People

Everyone who has ever had a pet knows how sweet pet ownership can be. Whether the pet is a cat curled up in its owner's lap, a dog retrieving a tossed stick, or a squeaky guinea pig looking for a snack, the bond between pets and their people is a strong one.

Shall we dance?

Oh my, look what he pulled out of the hat!

Only their hairdresser knows!

True friends indeed!

How sweet it is!

SYNTHESIZING

Sweet Eats

Last night, Tamika's dad taught her how to make peanut treats. She watched and listened carefully so she could teach her classmates to make these treats the next day. She made a T-chart for her notes. Tamika wrote down the ingredients and the amounts as her dad measured them out. She also wrote down what her dad did and said, but she didn't write every detail. For instance, she didn't bother noting when her father dropped a spoon.

Then Tamika used the process of **synthesizing** to organize and reword her notes. She combined her notes with what she knew about cooking and recipes and wrote a report to share orally with her class.

Making Peanut Treats

Notes	My Report
$1\frac{1}{2}$ cups peanut butter	
$\frac{3}{4}$ cups honey.	
1 cup raisins or dried cherries	This is what you need for peanut treats:
$\frac{1}{2}$ cup sunflower seeds	
$\frac{1}{2}$ cup peanuts	
$\frac{1}{2}$ teaspoon vanilla extract	
$2\frac{1}{4}$ cups crispy rice cereal	

Notes	My Report
1. Put peanut butter into bowl. Add other items. Dump everything but the cereal together and squish it up.	1. Stir all ingredients except the cereal in a bowl.
2. Pour cereal into mixture. Don't mash the cereal when you pour it into the rest of the stuff.	2. Mix in the cereal. Be gentle.
3. Make little balls. Put them on a cookie sheet. Use a tablespoon, not a teaspoon.	3. Use a tablespoon to make balls. Put them on a cookie sheet.
4. Cover treats with plastic wrap. Put in refrigerator for one-half hour.	4. Cover peanut treats with plastic wrap and put them in the refrigerator for at least half an hour. Have plenty of napkins on hand because these yummy treats are messy to eat.

Hank and Gretchen

by Brad Herzog

This is the tale of Hank and Gretchen, who lived in a clean house on a clean street in a very clean town.

The town's name was Spotlessville, and it was uncommonly spotless. It had clean roads, clean rooms, even clean toads and clean brooms. By order of Mayor Spickandspan, there was also a law requiring clean teeth.

"Our teeth should be so white that they shine all the way to Messy Valley," said the mayor. Messy Valley was a town several miles away. It wasn't nearly as neat as Spotlessville.

Then Mayor Spickandspan announced, "From now on, no sweets are allowed in Spotlessville." With that, he put his tidy hat on his clean head and walked down an unsoiled path to his sparkling house.

Do you think it would be a good idea to outlaw sweets from your town? Why do you think that?

"No sweets?" cried Gretchen.

"No candy?" moaned Hank.

How Sweet It Is! **A19**

Over the next few weeks, they discussed the matter with the rest of the children of Spotlessville. They were all sour on the No Sweets Rule.

"I'm disappointed," said one.

"Discouraged!" said another.

"Displeased!" yelled a third. But they couldn't disobey their parents. That would be disrespectful.

Just then, Hank spotted something. It was big and dark and galloping through town. Could it be? Yes! There was no doubt about it. "It's a chocolate moose!" Hank shouted.

He and Gretchen grabbed their skateboards and followed behind. It was the middle of the day in the middle of the summer, and the sun was an oven heating the pavement. In fact, it was so hot that it was

easy for Hank and Gretchen to follow the chocolate moose. He was melting! Like an automobile leaking oil, he was leaving spots of chocolate throughout the town.

Hank and Gretchen followed the trail out of Spotlessville and all the way to Lost Forest. The forest wasn't lost, of course. Everybody knew where it was. No, it got its name because once people stepped into it, they could never seem to find their way out.

"We can't go in there. We'll never get out," said Gretchen.

"Sure we will," said Hank. "We can just follow the chocolate trail back." So they left their skateboards and followed the moose.

Little did they know that somebody else was following the trail, too. It was a man riding a shiny, silver, super-duper street cleaner. He was cleaning up the melted chocolate!

The street cleaner even followed them into the forest, but soon he decided to turn back. "Nobody ever gets out of Lost Forest," he said.

Meanwhile, the children pushed on. Later, Gretchen looked to see if the chocolate trail was still behind them. It was gone!

"What are we going to do?" she whispered. The forest trees were a dense umbrella covering everything in darkness. Gretchen was getting scared.

Would you follow that chocolate moose? What might make you change your mind?

"Let's keep following the moose's trail. He must be going somewhere," said Hank, who was just as scared as his sister.

But night arrived, the air grew colder, and the moose stopped melting. Hank and Gretchen were lost. They wandered in the forest for hours as the citizens of Spotlessville began to search for them.

Finally, after what seemed like miles, the children came to a clearing in the forest. Hank and Gretchen couldn't believe their eyes. There was the most delicious-looking house they had ever seen!

It had gingerbread walls, a butterscotch roof, and caramel windows. A peanut brittle diving board rose above a pool of cherry punch. There was even a cupcake trampoline in back.

The children tiptoed to the door and looked inside. The first thing they noticed was that the chocolate moose had melted to the size of a mouse! He was talking to a piece of orange taffy.

"Gee, Moose," said the taffy, "I told you it was too hot for a scouting party today. Look how much you've melted."

The children were stunned. Not only was there talking taffy, there was licorice lounging on a loveseat, bubblegum bouncing on a bed, and a candy cane cleaning the carpet. The sweets were just as surprised to see Hank and Gretchen.

"Wow, have we missed you!" said the taffy. "Ever since your head of government, the mayor, banned us from town, we've had to live here in the forest. It's no fun at all."

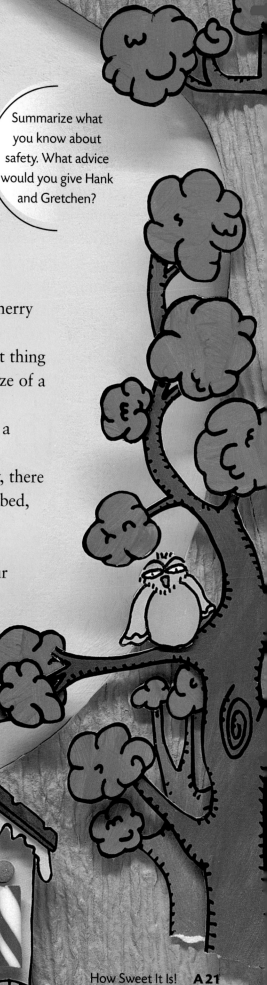

Summarize what you know about safety. What advice would you give Hank and Gretchen?

"Gee, I knew that children missed candy. I never realized candy missed children, too," said Gretchen.

"Sure we do!" said a peppermint stick. "What good is candy without children to enjoy it? We miss Spotlessville."

"So do we!" said Hank, and he told them how the chocolate trail had disappeared. "We'll never get home," he frowned.

But the sweets just smiled and said, "We can get you back."

The sweets went right to work building a magical machine. It had wheels made of cookies, a candy bar floor, and a marshmallow seat. The final piece was a lollipop steering wheel.

"Hop on!" shouted Moose, who scurried on board.

The wind whipped through the children's hair as they rode through the forest in their candy car. The trees went past in a blur. Hank and Gretchen felt like they were flying.

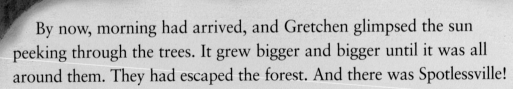

By now, morning had arrived, and Gretchen glimpsed the sun peeking through the trees. It grew bigger and bigger until it was all around them. They had escaped the forest. And there was Spotlessville!

The whole town turned out to greet the children. The people cheered. The children's parents wept with joy. And then the mayor arrived.

He hugged Hank and Gretchen, turned to the sweets who had saved them, and smiled. "From now on," he declared, "there will always be candy in Spotlessville!"

The taffy jumped for joy. The candy cane danced with the lollipop. "Home, sweet home," said Moose.

And they all ate happily ever after. ○

Has your thinking about outlawing sweets changed after reading this story? Why or why not?

Forbidden Treats

Why did Mayor Spickandspan of Spotlessville decide to forbid sweets? Surely he had more on his mind than shiny white teeth! Pretend you are the mayor. Give a persuasive speech to your classmates to convince them that sweet treats should be forbidden.

Follow That Moose!

Read the original fairy tale, "Hansel and Gretel." Then compare the fairy tale with the story about Hank and Gretchen. Make a Venn diagram to show what is the same and what is different between the two stories. Share and compare your completed diagram with a classmate.

The House That Moose Built

Can't you just taste the chocolate moose's house with its gingerbread walls, butterscotch roof, and caramel windows? Use milk cartons or small boxes and make a house. Decorate the house with pictures of your favorite foods.

Wildlife Watching

by Diane Bair and Pamela Wright

Hungry? Looking for something yummy to munch? How about a big plate of seaweed, a tall glass of pond juice, or a generous helping of raw deer meat?

If this doesn't sound like a sweet treat to you, don't worry. These foods are not meant for humans. They are delicacies, however, for three fascinating animals: manatees, moose, and wolves.

Let's go on three animal-watching adventures to see these animals. We'll swim with manatees in Florida. We'll look for moose in Maine. We'll track wolves in Minnesota. Don't worry. It's safe if you join an animal-watching trip lead by an experienced guide.

Use a three-column chart to list what you learn about each animal.

Snorkeling with Manatees

"Put on your mask and fins and slip quietly into the water," John, our guide, instructs us. Froglike, with flippered feet in the air, we tumble off the side of the pontoon boat. The water is a blanket wrapping us in warmth. We float around on the surface for a few minutes. Then, we adjust our masks and look into the murky green water.

We don't see them in the unclear water. But, in a few minutes, the water begins to roil, swirling and churning around us. Suddenly, we're face-to-snout with a 10-foot long, 1,000-pound manatee. Even through a foggy face mask, we can see its lumpy snout, tiny round eyes, whiskered lips, and grinning mouth. The manatee quickly swims away, but in seconds another manatee approaches us. And then another. We are surrounded by manatees, at least 60 of them, sharing the same warm waters.

Each winter, one of the largest herds of West Indian manatees in the United States migrates to the warm, spring-fed waters of the Crystal and Homosassa Rivers in Florida. Manatees are mammals, so during the coldest months of the year (when the water temperature dips below 68° F), they look for warmer water. Many come from the Gulf of Mexico, arriving around mid-November and staying until mid-March. Approximately 250 to 300 manatees come to loll in the springs and feed on some of their favorite food treats—leafy, aquatic plants.

Although they look like seals with grayish plump bodies and a paddle-shaped tail, manatees are actually related to elephants. They average about 13 feet long and can weigh up to 3,000 pounds. The manatees' only natural enemy is man. Manatees collide with fast-moving boats, get tangled in fishing gear, and get cut while eating vegetation that gets wrapped around boat propellers.

"Manatees are the most gentle creatures on Earth," our guide tells us. "They never hurt people."

Still, at first we're nervous about swimming with these giant sea cows. Soon we begin to relax. The best approach, we discover, is to lie limp as a water lily and let the manatees take the lead. Some manatees are coy and avoid us. Others treat us like water toys, nudging us, diving beneath us, rubbing up against us, and circling from side to front for a surprise pop-up. The manatees have the advantage in this game. Their mud-colored bodies blend in with the muddy water and grasses, so we can't see them until they're really close.

After a couple of hours of play, we hoist ourselves back in the boat, and say goodbye to our new friends—the manatees.

List three things you learned about manatees.

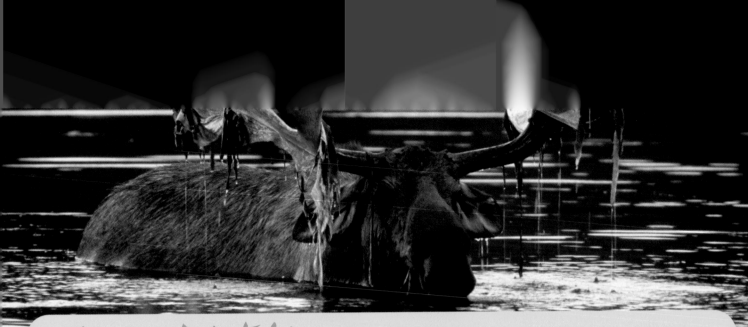

Moose Watching

It is early morning, one of the best times to see moose. This is when moose come out of the woods to feed in shallow waters. The sun's first rays shine through the trees and glisten off the shimmering lake waters. The air drips with the smell of wet wood and pine.

We're in kayaks, paddling Moosehead Lake in northern Maine. Everywhere we look there is evidence of moose. We notice broken tree branches along the shoreline. The trampled soil is littered with hundreds of moose tracks.

We glide the kayaks quietly into a shallow stream, ducking under low branches. We are careful not to make any noise. As we round a corner, we see a huge bull moose. He dunks his long, wrinkled snout into the water to nibble on pond weeds. Then he lifts his head and looks our way. His antlers are dripping with stringy, wet weeds. We stop paddling but our kayaks float within a few yards of the moose. We stare in disbelief as it lumbers into the dark woods.

"He was giant!" someone in our group exclaims.

"Humongous!" someone else adds.

"That was unbelievable!" another shouts.

Maine is one of the best places in the country to see moose in the wild. Moose like Maine's abundant forests and wetland areas. They feed on twigs and weeds in the winter. During warm months, they eat the plants in shallow lakes and ponds.

Many people are surprised when they first see a moose. They may not realize how big they are. Moose can be up to 10 feet long and almost 8 feet tall. Male moose, called bulls, usually weigh between 1,200 and 1,600 pounds. Females usually weigh between 800 and 1,300 pounds. Moose have long skinny legs, big heads, and huge overhanging muzzles. A flap of skin, called the bell, hangs beneath their throats. Male moose have large, spoon-shaped antlers that are spiked on the end.

We paddle for another hour or so, sighting several moose along the way, including a mother and her calf. Some moose scurry quickly out of sight when they see us. Others stand inactive for several minutes, treating us to close-up views. As we near the end of our moose-watching trip, our guide shouts, "A moose!" There it was—a moose swimming in the middle of the lake. "You don't see that often," our guide tells us. But, we did!

List three things you learned about moose.

Tracking Wolves

We're hovering above the Superior National Forest in a four-seater prop plane. Below us, we see snowladen evergreens, frozen lakes, and icy swamps. The snowy winterscape is a dazzling diamond, shining so brightly that it hurts our eyes. We're on an adventure, flying along the border of the Boundary Waters Wilderness Area tracking gray wolves. Here, in the dense, wet forests of northern Minnesota, more than 2,000 wolves run wild and free. It's the largest concentration in the continental United States.

Within minutes, we pick up a signal from one of the radio-collared wolves. It is unclear where the signal is coming from at first. When it grows stronger, we know we're headed in the right direction. Seconds later we see them. "There! There!" we shout. We see dark red splotches staining the white snowfields and leading to a recent kill site. . . and, in clear view, a pack of six wolves. We watch as the wolf pack destroys and devours a fallen deer. To a wolf, raw deer meat is a favorite treat.

Our flight is one of the activities included in the wolf-watching weekends offered at the International Wolf Center in Ely, Minnesota. You don't have to be a scientist to join in this animal-watching adventure. Anyone is welcome.

The adventure begins with a snowshoe trek into the woods in search of radio-collared wolves. The scientists at the wolf center rely on radio tracking to learn about wolves. Wolves equipped with collars are tracked by signals. Information on their movement and activity helps in the study of wolf behavior.

We snowshoe through deep snow for about a half-hour when we spot something. We stoop down to get a closer look at a fresh set of animal tracks. They are definitely wolf tracks, our guide informs us. Some people in the group are displeased about finding the tracks. What if we find the wolf? Won't it be unsafe?

Our guide, an expert in wolf behavior, explains that wolves usually run from people. If they hear us coming, the wolves will quickly disappear into the woods.

We follow the tracks and soon pick up a faint radio signal from a wolf. "Is he nearby?" someone in the group asks. But the signal stops. We find more tracks but head out of the woods without seeing a wolf.

"Don't be unhappy or disappointed," our guide tells us. "It's very unusual to come upon a wolf in the woods."

We end our adventure with a twilight wolf howl. We stand at the edge of a deep, dark forest. We creep up to the edge of the woods, turn our faces to the darkening sky, open our mouths, and let out a loud, lingering *A-oooo, A-oooo.* Nothing. We try again. *A-oooo, A-oooo.* Silence. One more time, we howl to the silent wolves. *A-oooo, A-oooo.* Through the trees comes the wild, stretched-out howls of a wolf. "Ah, you're one of the lucky ones," our guide tells us. "Wolves don't always answer back. What a sweet ending to our adventure. ○

List three things you learned about wolves.

Summarize in three sentences what you have learned about manatees, moose, and wolves.

You Choose The One

Suppose your class is planning to go on one of the three animal adventures described in the article. Which one should it be? Use a web to show the reasons why you prefer one of the animal adventures. Synthesize your ideas and write a paragraph explaining your choice. Then share your paragraph with your class.

People Watching

What do animals think when people come to observe them in the wild? Be a manatee, moose, or wolf in your natural home. Packs of human visitors arrive from time to time to take a look at you. How do you respond? Are you feeling exasperated, flattered, indifferent, or something else? Write a letter to the Wilderness Gazette to express your feelings.

Frame That Animal!

Find photos of manatees, moose, and wolves in library books and study them carefully. Then draw portraits of one, two, or all three of the animals. You may want to make frames for your animal portraits using twigs, ice-cream sticks, or other materials.

What Am I?

It's fun to put riddles into poems. Which animal is described in this riddle poem?

> Dusty gray ears flap forward, flap back.
> Wrinkled tree-trunk legs lean left, lean right.
> A peanut, a shower, a trumpeting call.
> Compared to you, I'm very tall.

You knew the answer was an elephant, didn't you! How many lines did you read before you figured it out?

Try writing an animal riddle poem of your own. Keep it short—no more than six lines. Use just a few words to sum up some of the things you know and feel about the animal. The trick is to give a few good clues so the riddle is not impossible to figure out. But if you give too many clues, the riddle will be too easy.

Yum!

What's your all-time favorite dessert? Draw a picture and write a yummy description.

Super Sundae

As dessert chef at the Roly Poly Restaurant, your job is to invent a new sundae. Write a name for your delicious sundae and explain how to make it step-by-step.

Wanted: Perfect Pet

Do you already have a perfect pet? Do you want one? Make a wanted poster. Begin by writing the title "Wanted: Perfect Pet." Draw a portrait of the pet and write a few identifying qualities under its picture.

More Books

Alderson, Brian. *Cakes and Custard.* W. Morrow, 1974.

Catling, Patrick Skene. *The Chocolate Touch.* Dell, 1996.

Gardella, Tricia. *Writers in the Kitchen: Children's Book Authors Share Memories of Their Favorite Recipes.* Boyds Mill Press, 1998.

Greenfield, Eloise. *Honey, I Love and Other Love Poems.* Crowell, 1986.

Marshall, James. *Hansel and Gretel.* Puffin, 1994.

Naylor, Phyllis Reynolds. *Beetles, Lightly Toasted.* Atheneum, 1987.

On the Web

Sweet Treats
http://www.candyusa.org
http://www.kidscandy.org
http://www.kidscook.com

Cool and Creamy Ice Cream
http://www.makeicecream.com
http://www.foodsci.uoguelph.ca/
   dairyedu/icecream.html

Bug Cuisine
http://www.eatbug.com

Animal Watching
http://www.sandiegozoo.org
http://birminghamzoo.com/ao/

Across the Curriculum

Science/Health

Everyone knows that sugar is sweet, but too much of it causes tooth decay. Why is that? Find out and share what you learn with the rest of the class in a demonstration or a written report.

Social Studies

What sweet treats did American children eat long ago? Find a dessert recipe from a century or so ago that has ingredients you can find in grocery stores today. Ask an adult to help you follow the recipe to make the dessert. Then enjoy your historic treat together.

Cricket Crepes, Anyone?

When you first consider it, the thought of eating bugs may turn your stomach. But wait! Many kinds of bugs are healthful. They are chock-full of protein and low in fat, too. Still not convinced? Remember, what we like to eat is what we are used to eating. After all, it is OK to eat a burger made of beef or vegetables, so why not a mealworm burger?

If you decide to have a bug-eating adventure, you need to find out which bugs are good to eat, where you can get them, and how to prepare them. Do some research. Perhaps a vet or a specialist at a department of entomology at your local university or museum can help you figure out which bugs are good to eat and which ones to avoid. Workers at a zoo may know where you can buy bugs—after all, zoo animals eat thousands of bugs every day. You should have no trouble finding bug recipes. Ask a librarian to help you.

Some middle schoolers held a celebration of bug recipes recently. Here are a few of the delicacies they sampled: mealworm spaghetti, cricket lollipops, bug brownies, chocolate cricket torte, larvae latkes (pancakes), chocolate chirpy chip cookies, and bugs-in-a-rug (crickets and pineapple pieces wrapped in bacon). If these bug dishes sound tempting, get to work, and you'll soon be eating bugs for brunch.

You Don't Say!

THINK ABOUT: Monitoring

NONFICTION
A Town Named Sue
Travel the country and discover odd-named towns.

B11

FICTION
Words of Wisdom
Max overflows with words. Find out why.

B4

FICTION
The Jingle
Read about the jingle contest.

B19

NONFICTION
What Did You Say?
What are idioms and where do they come from?

B25

MONITORING

The Poetry Contest

Does your teacher ever tell you to monitor your behavior at a school assembly? Or maybe you've been a hall monitor, making sure students are quiet in the hallways. You **monitor** your reading, also. When we read, we monitor, or check, to make sure our reading makes sense.

When you read for information, it's important to read carefully. If the information is especially important or confusing, you might reread or review what you've read to make sure you understand it. *Rereading* and *reviewing* are fix-up strategies readers use. Sometimes you also need to *read on* to understand what you're reading.

Read the ad below about a poetry contest. Think about how many times you *reread, review,* or *read on* to monitor your reading.

Hey, Cyber Poets! Win a Computer!

Win a new computer! Write a 6- to 8-line rhyming poem about how a computer helps you learn. Your poem should include three reasons why computers are important to your education. The poem must be an original—not something written by a famous poet, your sister, or your dog. Type your poem, double-spaced, using 1-inch margins. On the upper right-hand corner, type your name, address (snail mail *and* e-mail), and phone number. E-mail it to the address listed below by

Reread and *review* the ad to make sure you understand the contest. Then list the contest rules. How did you do?

Think about monitoring when you read other things today. As you read your social studies book or your library book, notice how you monitor your reading. When do you *review, reread,* and *read on* to understand better?

WORDS of WISDOM

by Jeanette McMahon

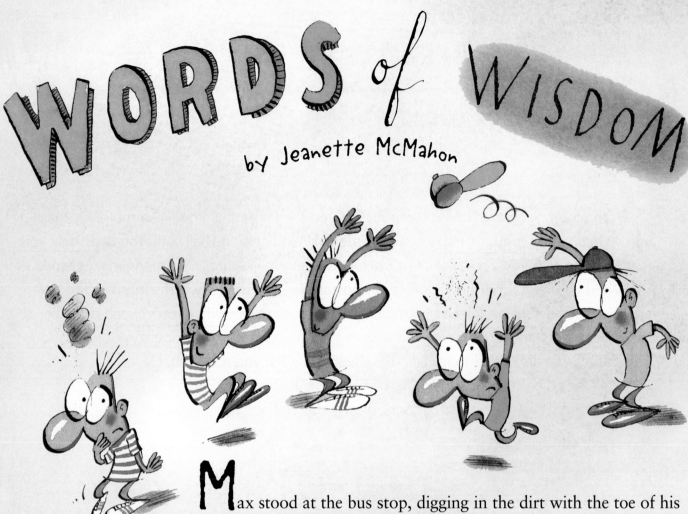

Max stood at the bus stop, digging in the dirt with the toe of his tennis shoe. A group of girls stood in a tight circle nearby, their voices sounding like twittering bluebirds. A bunch of boys stood in another group, waving Tom Finley's baseball hat in the air. But Tom was outnumbered and couldn't get his hat back.

Max heard the roar of the bus as it approached. He knew it would be noisy on the bus, but that didn't bother him. Max always lost himself in a book, anyway. Max loved to read. He read books about space exploration and NASA missions. He read spy stories from the FBI and CIA files. He read historical books, sports books, and all sorts of other books. He had loved reading from the time he was old enough to turn the page and knew he'd never outgrow it. His head was always full of words from the books he read, but he had an overwhelming fear of speaking—he never knew quite what to say.

Once on the bus, Max slid into a seat and got out his newest book—one about Ben Franklin. Tom Finley got on last, sat down beside Max, and dusted off his returned hat. Max wanted to say something to Tom. Instead, he just gripped his book a little tighter and continued to read.

At lunchtime, Max stood silently in the cafeteria line. The cafeteria worker plopped food onto a plate. Max brought the plate down from the counter and placed it on his tray. He looked at the food. It looked like chop suey.

"Oh well," thought Max. He really didn't like chop suey, but he carried the tray to a table anyway. He picked at a noodle with his fork. Then he saw the fortune cookie on his tray. He cracked the cookie open and devoured it, almost forgetting to read his fortune. He smoothed out the crumpled piece of paper and read: "Others will flock to hear your words of wisdom."

What clues has the author already given you to help you decide if Max's fortune was an appropriate one for him?

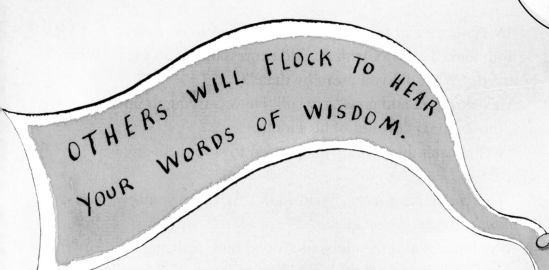

OTHERS WILL FLOCK TO HEAR YOUR WORDS OF WISDOM.

"Boy, I sure got the wrong fortune," Max thought to himself as he removed the tray from the table.

The next morning before school, Max walked past his brother's room and noticed he was still in bed. *"Early to bed and early to rise, makes a man healthy, wealthy, and wise,"* Max said.

Max clamped his hand over his mouth; his eyes opened wide. He had no idea where those words had come from. They had just popped out of his mouth!

At the bus stop, Max saw Tom Finley again. He noticed Tom was not wearing his baseball hat.

"Where's your hat?" Max asked shyly.

"I didn't feel like chasing after it today, so I left it at home," replied Tom. "I keep thinking I'll stand up to those bullies tomorrow."

Reread the quote Max just used. Why did he seem so surprised by what he said?

NEVER LEAVE THAT TILL TOMORROW...

"*Never leave that till tomorrow which you can do today,*" said Max.

Tom looked at Max with an odd expression on his face. "What?" he asked. "What did you mean by that?"

Max shrugged and grew very still. He was trying to understand how those words flew out of his mouth.

"Well, I can't think of anything to do to stop them anyway," sighed Tom.

"*Thinking is hard work,*" said Max. "*Whether you think you can or think you can't—you are right.*"

Max blushed and then looked around him, realizing suddenly that those words had come from him. The words sounded familiar—but where had he heard them before?

Then Max had an idea. "*Float like a butterfly and sting like a bee,*" he suggested, but he knew fighting was not the answer.

"I'm not Muhammed Ali and I don't know how to box," said Tom. "Besides, I'm afraid of bees. But maybe YOU could talk to them."

Review the story so far. How is Max coming up with these great quotes?

"Well . . .," Max started to say. Talk to them? Talking was the one thing Max didn't know how to do very well, even though lately all these great words were falling from his mouth. Then he remembered his favorite part of *Owl Moon*: "When you go owling you don't need words or warm or anything but hope." Maybe with lots of hope (and a few words) he could help Tom.

Max told Tom he had an idea. He would outline a plan ASAP and tell Tom about it the next morning. Tom looked relieved. "Thanks for helping me out," Tom said.

"Don't count your chickens before they are hatched," Max replied with a smile. "And don't forget to wear your baseball hat."

That night, the light in Max's room was on until very late. He had begun to put two and two together. By morning, his desk was overflowing with books.

Max was a little nervous walking to the bus stop. He hoped he had not miscalculated the situation.

"The only thing we have to fear is fear itself," Max told himself.

When he turned the corner, Max saw that the other boys were already tossing Tom's hat around. He took a deep breath and stepped into the middle of the crowd of boys.

"The buck stops here," Max said firmly.

The other boys were so surprised to hear Max speak that they stopped throwing Tom's hat and turned and stared right at Max. Max took a deep breath and spoke again.

"I have a dream that one day this nation will rise up and live out the true meaning of its creed: 'We hold these truths to be self-evident—that all men are created equal.'"

What does it mean to miscalculate a situation? Try rereading or reading on to figure it out.

No one moved. Then one of the boys silently picked up the hat, dusted it off, and handed it back to Tom. The others just stood there with their mouths open.

"Thanks," Tom said quietly.

"Well," said Max, *"that's one small step for man, one giant leap for mankind."*

Just then the bus pulled up. Tom turned to the group of boys and smirked. Then he got on the bus with Max.

As they started off for school, Tom grinned at Max.

"That was great," he said. "I guess I misjudged those guys. They aren't so bad after all."

"In spite of everything, I still believe people are good at heart," said Max.

"Yeah, but how did you know what to say?" asked Tom.

Max did have an idea about the answer to that one, but he just shrugged and put his hands in his pockets. He felt a crumpled piece of paper and took it out. It was the fortune from his fortune cookie. He reread it. "Others will flock to hear your words of wisdom." Max had overcome his fear. His fortune had come true after all.

Max finally could say the right things, but he realized that doing the right thing was just as important. He knew helping Tom with this little mishap was a job well done. And after all, *"Well done is better than well said."* ⬤

How will Max answer Tom's question? Read on to find out.

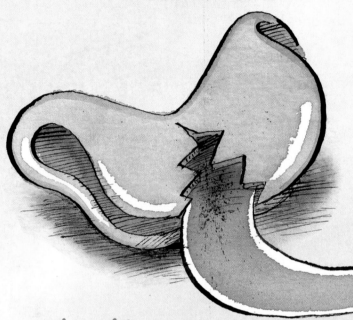

Your Family's Fortunes

Each member of your family is about to open a fortune cookie. What would each of their fortunes say, and why? Share your fortunes with a partner.

Write About It

In your journal, write about one of the quotations Max used. Write down your thoughts about what it means to you. Was it the right thing to say in the situation? Why or why not?

Words to Live By

Find a book of quotations and choose one piece of advice that you think will help you keep a positive attitude during the school day. Write down the quotation using a cool computer font or hand-lettering. Display your quotation on your desk or on the cover of your notebook.

Words for the Wise

A proverb is a popular saying that describes a basic truth or rule of behavior. Every culture has its favorite proverbs, such as the ones below.

African Proverbs

The moon moves slowly, but it crosses the town.

Money is sharper than a sword.

When spider webs unite, they can tie up a lion.

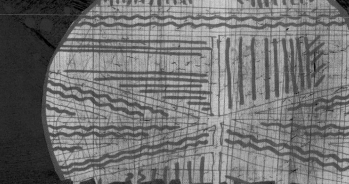

Chinese Proverbs

A book is like a garden carried in the pocket.

No wind, no waves.

There are many paths to the top of the mountain, but the view is always the same.

Native American Proverbs

We will be known forever by the tracks we leave. (Dakota)

Don't let yesterday use up too much of today. (Cherokee)

One finger cannot lift a pebble. (Hopi)

Choose one of the proverbs above and write a few paragraphs in your journal to describe what you think it means.

A Town Named Sue

by Brad Herzog

Have you ever wondered how towns get their names? Apparently, lots of other people do, too. In fact, there's even a word for this type of wondering. The study of place-names is called **toponomy**, from the Greek words "topos," meaning "place," and "onyma," meaning "name."

Did you have to read on to find out what *toponomy* meant?

Often, cities and towns are named after important people. It might be the first person to settle the town or the last person to leave before the new settlers arrived. Sometimes, the names describe whatever draws people to the area, like a river or an ocean. Some examples of towns like this are *Pleasant Valley, Lake Charles,* and *Long Beach.*

If you take a trip across a map of the United States, you can also find hundreds of towns with strange names that came from unexpected places. For example, in 1950, the city of *Hot Springs,* New Mexico, was renamed after a popular radio game show, *Truth or Consequences.* Can you imagine a city named *Who Wants to be a Millionaire*? It sounds impossible, but you never know . . . .

Perhaps you have heard of a large city like *Buffalo,* New York. But what about *Flamingo,* Florida, or *Turkey,* Texas, or *Bald Eagle,* Minnesota? Nearly every state in the U.S. has at least one town named after an animal. There is an *Alligator* in Mississippi, a *Bear* in Delaware, and a *Dinosaur* in Colorado. I wonder if that town's name has been around since prehistoric times! There's even a *Chicken* in Alaska! It seems that residents wanted to name their town after the state bird, but since no one could pronounce "ptarmigan," they called it *Chicken* instead.

Humansville, Missouri, is named after people in general, but many towns reflect one person's name. For example, the California town of *Susanville* calls itself the "Susans Capital of the World." In the summer of 2000, Susanville held a festival honoring anyone named Susan.

There are many other towns around the country that also go by common first names. In fact, there is a good a chance you can find one named after you! Is your name Max? Maybe you should visit *Max,* North Dakota. Is your name Meredith? Look up *Meredith,* New Hampshire. Go to Utah and discover *Roy.* Visit Ohio and a town named *Ashley.* Where's *Waldo*? Why, that's a town in Florida. In the state of Texas alone, there are towns named *Alice, Bryan,*

Clyde, Donna, Ennis, Gordon, Inez, Joshua, Kyle, Louise, Melissa, Terrell, Victoria, and *Winnie.* Whew!

Sometimes places have names that seem like common words but are actually named after people, like *Faith,* South Dakota, and *Honor,*

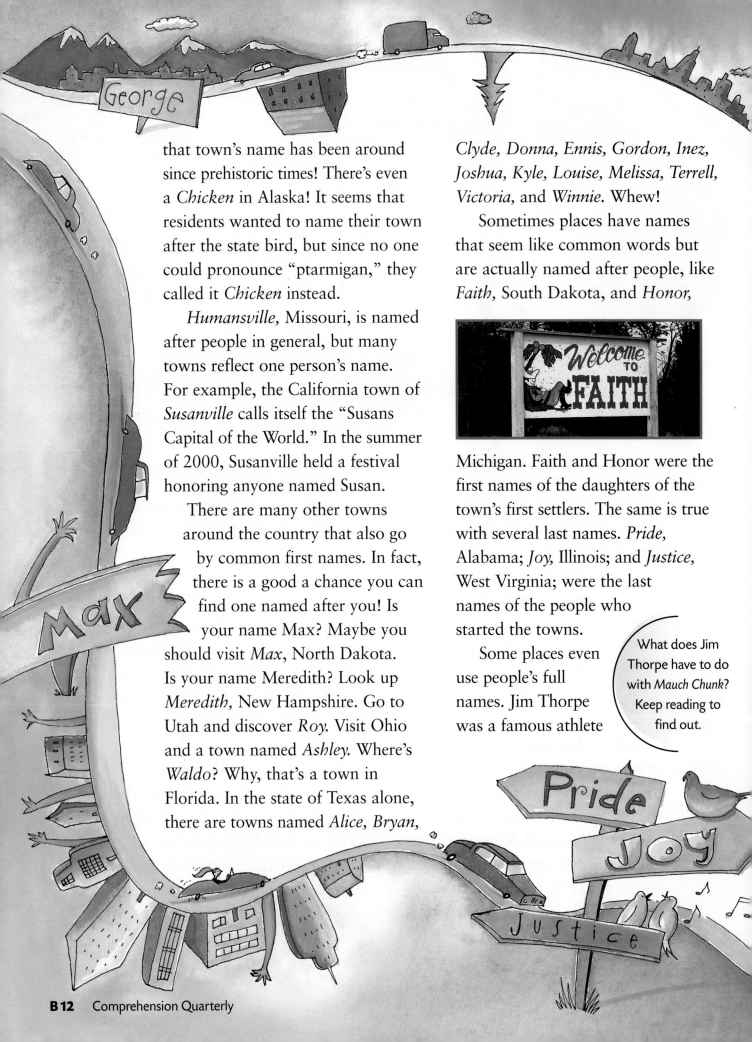

Michigan. Faith and Honor were the first names of the daughters of the town's first settlers. The same is true with several last names. *Pride,* Alabama; *Joy,* Illinois; and *Justice,* West Virginia; were the last names of the people who started the towns.

Some places even use people's full names. Jim Thorpe was a famous athlete

What does Jim Thorpe have to do with *Mauch Chunk*? Keep reading to find out.

in the early 1900s. In 1953, a town called *Mauch Chunk* agreed to change its name so that it could be the site of Thorpe's grave. Today, the town is known as *Jim Thorpe*, Pennsylvania. You can also visit *Robert Lee*, Texas, and *Captain Cook*, Hawaii. There's even a town named *George* in the state of Washington. That's right—*George*, Washington!

Many town names include numbers. There is *Two Harbors*, Minnesota; *Three Rivers*, California; *Four Oaks*, North Carolina; and *Five Points*, New Mexico. One town in Wyoming is called *Ten Sleep*, but more than 10 people live there— 300 is more like it.

A trip around the country can also turn into an awesome five-course meal. First you'll need *Forks*, Washington, and a *Spooner*, Wisconsin. Then you can find *Toast*, North Carolina; *Corn*, Oklahoma; and *Walnut*, California on the menu, not to mention *Hamburg*, New Jersey, and *Fries*, Virginia. You can pick a *Tangerine* in Florida and a *Plum* in

Pennsylvania, or you can exchange all of them for a visit to *Fruitland*, Idaho. Afterward, don't forget to wash them down with *Hot Coffee*, Mississippi; *Tea*, South Dakota; or *Cocoa*, Florida.

Most towns like to attract visitors. That's why the people who name the towns often pick happy names, like *Happy*, Texas. They want to show that it's an OK place to visit, like *Okay*, Oklahoma. You can shorten that one to *Okay*, OK!

A long time ago, the ranchers who lived on the California coast frequently argued over their dairy businesses. They finally decided the feuding was useless and instead, vowed they would live in harmony. It only made sense to name their town *Harmony*. Today, *Harmony* is home to many artists.

Reread about the ranchers' feud to see if you agree with what they named the town.

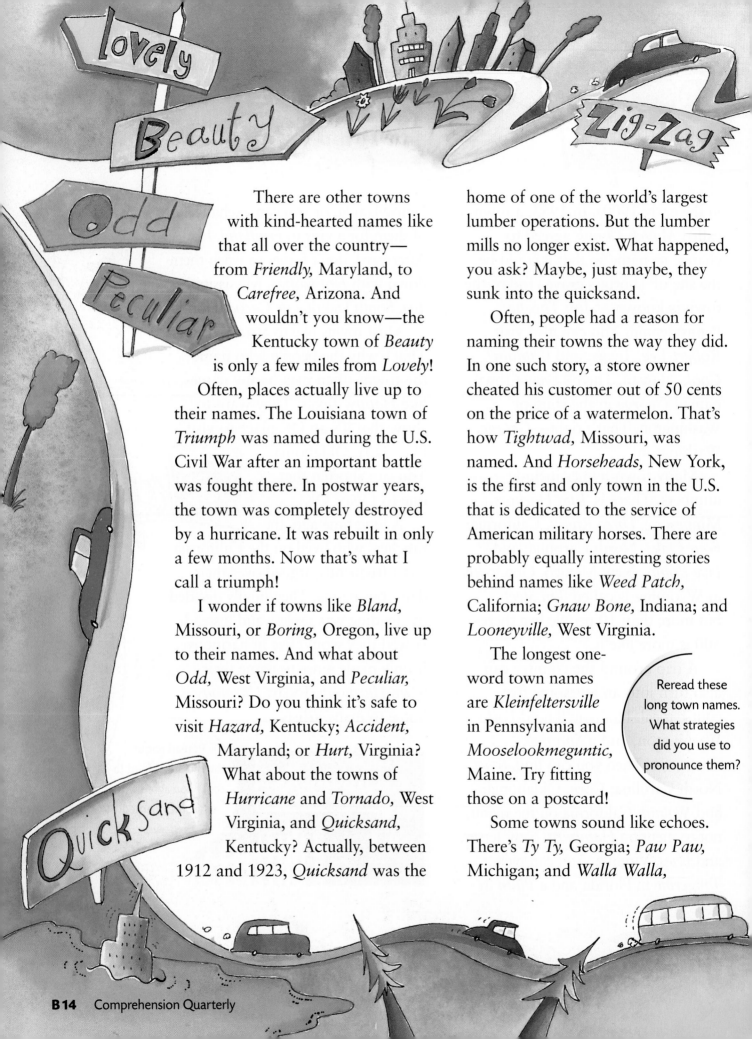

There are other towns with kind-hearted names like that all over the country—from *Friendly,* Maryland, to *Carefree,* Arizona. And wouldn't you know—the Kentucky town of *Beauty* is only a few miles from *Lovely!* Often, places actually live up to their names. The Louisiana town of *Triumph* was named during the U.S. Civil War after an important battle was fought there. In postwar years, the town was completely destroyed by a hurricane. It was rebuilt in only a few months. Now that's what I call a triumph!

I wonder if towns like *Bland,* Missouri, or *Boring,* Oregon, live up to their names. And what about *Odd,* West Virginia, and *Peculiar,* Missouri? Do you think it's safe to visit *Hazard,* Kentucky; *Accident,* Maryland; or *Hurt,* Virginia? What about the towns of *Hurricane* and *Tornado,* West Virginia, and *Quicksand,* Kentucky? Actually, between 1912 and 1923, *Quicksand* was the home of one of the world's largest lumber operations. But the lumber mills no longer exist. What happened, you ask? Maybe, just maybe, they sunk into the quicksand.

Often, people had a reason for naming their towns the way they did. In one such story, a store owner cheated his customer out of 50 cents on the price of a watermelon. That's how *Tightwad,* Missouri, was named. And *Horseheads,* New York, is the first and only town in the U.S. that is dedicated to the service of American military horses. There are probably equally interesting stories behind names like *Weed Patch,* California; *Gnaw Bone,* Indiana; and *Looneyville,* West Virginia.

The longest one-word town names are *Kleinfeltersville* in Pennsylvania and *Mooselookmeguntic,* Maine. Try fitting those on a postcard!

Some towns sound like echoes. There's *Ty Ty,* Georgia; *Paw Paw,* Michigan; and *Walla Walla,*

> Reread these long town names. What strategies did you use to pronounce them?

Washington. Others sound like weird noises—like *Gackle*, North Dakota; *Bim*, West Virginia; *Opp*, Alabama; *Tok*, Alaska; *Zook*, Kansas; and *Zap*, North Dakota.

Other names don't make much sense at all. *Center*, Texas, is located nowhere near the center of the state. *Zigzag*, Oregon, can be found along a very straight road. And it often gets up to 100°F in *Cool*, California!

Even the location of some towns can be confusing. Many places on state borders are a mix of names. The city between Texas and Arkansas is called *Texarkana*. Where might you find the town of *Texico*? That's right, it's between Texas and New Mexico. The town of *Stateline*, Nevada, is located right along the state line that separates Nevada and California.

Even more confusing, many towns are names of different states. For example, a town named *Wyoming* can be found in seven states but not in the state of Wyoming. You can visit *Florida* in New York, *Iowa* in Louisiana, and *Michigan* in North Dakota. There is a *Virginia* in Minnesota, a *Nevada* in Texas, and a *Delaware* in Ohio. Confused?

Many towns carry the names of other countries, too. You don't need a passport to travel to *Canada*, Kentucky; *Mexico*, Maine; *Brazil*, Indiana; *Holland*, Ohio; *Scotland*, Pennsylvania; *Greece*, New York; or *Italy*, Texas. You can also visit *Norway*, Iowa; *Belgium*, Wisconsin; and *China*, Texas.

But why stop there? Explore a little further. You can do more than visit *Earth*, Texas, or *Moon*, Pennsylvania. You can take a trip to *Jupiter*, Florida; *Mars*, Pennsylvania; *Neptune*, New Jersey; and even *Star*, Idaho.

But wherever you go, you can always return to your favorite place. In fact, in Oregon it's the name of a town—*Sweet Home*. ○

Read on to explore a little further. Hint: take your space helmet with you!

Stop and Respond

Choose Your Words

Find an interesting town name in your state, and with a partner, make up a story about how the name came to be. Then write to the town's chamber of commerce or use the Internet to find the real story. Share your story with the class.

Poetic in Paris, Texas

Reread the article "A Town Named Sue." Pick three or four town names that you think are funny or interesting. Write a five-line poem or song that lists the names or focuses on just one name. Your poem might be serious, informative, or just plain silly. Share your poem with the class.

The Sights to See in Sue

Pick one of the towns described in "A Town Named Sue." Use the information from the article or do some quick research to find out more about the town. Design a one-page travel brochure convincing people to visit the town. Use magazine cut-outs or draw your own pictures to illustrate your brochure.

A LICENSE TO UNRAVEL

One way that people express themselves is by creating vanity license plates—or automobile license plates that cleverly combine letters and numbers to communicate (KMUNIK8) an idea. Sometimes the meaning on the license plate is clear. Sometimes you have to read carefully to figure it out. Translate the license plates here. Who do you think might be the owners of these cars? Then try your hand at creating your own vanity license plate (use up to seven letters or numbers).

3 CALIFORNIA
EZ BB LATE

4 OREGON
OB1CNOB

5 MAINE
IFXTVCR

6 INDIANA
ZIPNBY

1 IDAHO
IW84NO1

2 ILLINOIS
SLMDNK

7 FLORIDA
1DRFL

MONITORING

The Man of the House

When we read, we **monitor** our reading. Sometimes the monitoring we do involves changing our mind from the beginning to the end of a piece. Have you ever thought the main character of a story was just like you, but at the end you realized that you're not at all alike? That's monitoring. We often change our minds as we get further into a story.

Scott, age 10, was the youngest of four siblings. Mary was 11. Tara was 13. And Hope was 16. The only boy in a house with three sisters, his mom, and his grandma.

As Scott grew up in this household of girls, all his friends felt sorry for him. Scott always laughed it off, though. It really wasn't so bad.

His grandma kept him in stitches with her old sayings. For instance, when she went to the store, she'd say, "I'm off like a herd of turtles." And she was. After dinner, she'd pat her belly and say, "I'm fatter than a tick on a coon dog." Scott laughed—his grandma was skinny like a stick.

His mom was great, too. She shared stories about his dad's "barnstorming" days so Scott could learn about the dad he never knew. Scott dreamed of learning to fly and doing loops, rolls, and tailspins just like his dad.

His sisters were another story. Mary and Tara drove him nuts. They always took forever primping in the bathroom. Yet, all in all, they left Scott alone. His sister, Hope, was great, though. The two of them always worked on model planes together. For a big sister, she was pretty cool . . . .

If I were Scott, how would I feel about all those girls in the house?

Scott seems okay with his situation. Do I still feel sorry for him? Why?

Scott seems to have fun with his grandma. That's one way he's lucky.

Here it is. This is what I expected Scott to complain about.

Hope and Scott have a lot in common. At first, I thought it would be tough for Scott to be the only male in the house. As I read, I changed my mind. He seems to be okay with that.

Practice monitoring as you read the next story. Think about how your thoughts change along the way. Then talk with a partner about your experience.

The Jingle

by Judith Diamond

Roses are red.
Violets are blue.
Danny's so cute,
Don't you think so, too?

Alison bit on the end of her pencil and looked around the room. Everyone else was busy doing their math problems. But Alison was engrossed in her poetry writing. What else could she say about Danny? He was always so nice to her, but only Katie knew that she really liked him.

Katie poked her. "Hey, what are you writing?" she whispered.

"Just something. I'll tell you later," Alison whispered back.

"No, let me see now," Katie insisted. "I'm bored."

Alison folded her paper the special fancy way that only she and Katie knew how to do. "Here."

Katie carefully unfolded the note and giggled. "I hope Danny doesn't see this," she scribbled.

"Let me read it," said Audrey, grabbing for the note. Then Audrey gave it to Billy, who gave it to Paul, who drew a little cartoon of Danny and Alison on the back. Charlie snatched the note and threw it at Sawyer.

> What do you think about Alison's poetry? Why?

Mrs. Lawrence stopped talking. With a practiced eye, she swooped down and caught the note before it reached Sawyer. She turned to Alison and said, "See me at recess this afternoon."

Everyone was outside except Alison. Mrs. Lawrence was talking, and Alison was staring at her feet. ". . . pay attention . . . don't pass notes . . . surprised at you . . . Alison, look at me. How do you think Danny might be feeling? Wouldn't you be embarrassed if someone was passing around a note about you?"

Alison caught her breath. "I guess. I didn't mean to embarrass him. I'm sorry." Now Danny would probably hate her. She felt awful.

"Alison, I'll give you and the rest of the class a better reason to write something. Look." Mrs. Lawrence gave Alison a newspaper clipping. There, in all its glory, was a new set of state-of-the-art playground equipment. There were swings and slides and platforms and bridges. There were ropes and tires and bars. It was nothing like the old, beat-up equipment their school had now. Below the picture was the challenge: "To all kids in River City's 4th and 5th grades: Write a jingle about your city's Safe Neighborhood program, and win this playground for your school."

> What does the author mean by state-of-the-art playground equipment? Find clues to support your answer.

After lunch, Mrs. Lawrence passed the picture around and explained the details. The jingle had to be six to eight lines long and had to be sung. The students could work on the jingle individually, in pairs, or even in a small group. They had one month to write it.

Alison almost exploded. She LOVED writing poetry and jingles. It was her favorite pastime. She knew she could win the playground equipment for her school.

On the way home, Audrey, Alison, and Katie were so busy rhyming *crime* with *time* and *slime* and *dime* that they didn't see Sawyer and José on their bikes until they were right next to the girls. José did a wheelie. "You girls think you're so smart. Sawyer's going to beat all of you."

What do you think about the competition between Alison and Sawyer? Why?

"Oh, yeah?" exclaimed Katie. "I don't think so. Alison is the best writer in the class."

"Oh, yeah?" José copied her. "Ask Sawyer where he's going."

Sawyer didn't wait to be asked. "Guitar lessons," he said, and grinned. The boys rode off.

Audrey watched them and with wide eyes turned to Alison. "You have to sing it. You HATE to sing in music class. What are you going to do?"

For the next two weeks, the class worked on their jingles every afternoon. Most everyone was working in a group, but Alison and Sawyer worked alone.

In music class, Mr. Raulins even helped by pounding out TV jingles on the old piano. Once, Sawyer brought his guitar to school and accompanied Mr. Raulins on the piano. He WAS awesome. Alison squirmed.

Everyone buzzed with inspiration. Kids jumped rope to the jingles. They sang them on the way to school. Audrey, Katie, and Alison even traded ideas and made suggestions to each other.

Alison worked day and night on her jingle. She wrote on the bus to school, during lunch, and right up to dinnertime. Her mom and dad said they were tired of hearing rhymes at the dinner table. And her preschool brother began imitating her and driving EVERYONE crazy.

Two days before they had to stand up and present their jingles to the class, Alison had a dream. She was on a beautiful red bike racing down the hill like a plane accelerating down the runway, ready to soar into the sky. The wind was whipping her hair back, and people were cheering. Then someone called out, "Sing! Sing!" Suddenly, she was a large black crow sitting on a telephone wire. "Sing! Sing!" they shouted. Alison stretched her neck and opened her beak. All that came out was "SQUAWK!"

Her eyes flew open and she sat up in bed. "I can write, but singing is impossible," she thought desperately.

That day, after the bell, Alison stayed in her seat and waited for Mrs. Lawrence. The classroom door opened. But it wasn't Mrs. Lawrence—it was Sawyer.

"Alison," he said, slowly and uncomfortably, "I guess you're going to be happy. I'm quitting the contest."

"But why?" she asked. "You play so well. I'd give anything to play like that. I . . . I . . . I'm quitting, too."

"Well, I can't write like you can," Sawyer said. "Why would YOU quit? You were sure you were going to win," he asked her.

"I can't sing," replied Alison sadly.

There was silence as the idea slowly grew before them.

Two days later it was time for the presentations. Charlie was silly. Marilyn giggled. José was so scared that he sang softly and no one could hear him. Then Mrs. Lawrence said, "Our next presentation is a team effort."

Sawyer, Alison, and the guitar came to the front of the room. Sawyer sang and played as Alison held up the words on a big piece of posterboard. Hands down, the 4th and 5th grades thought theirs was the winner:

The Safe Neighborhood team is always there
To help us out when we need their care.
So if you see that something's wrong
Call them up, but don't wait too long.
The phone number's 555-6213—
Let's be as safe as we can be.

The class waited a very long two weeks. Every night as Alison, Katie, and Audrey walked home together, they made guesses about which school would win. They couldn't wait to get on the new playground equipment.

Finally, on the last Thursday before summer vacation, a telegram was delivered to Mrs. Lawrence. "I have good news, boys and girls," Mrs. Lawrence said, beaming. "Sawyer and Alison's jingle won second place in the contest."

"Second place?" Alison asked with disappointment. "We didn't win the new playground equipment?"

Mrs. Lawrence continued. "That's still something to be proud of, considering that children all over the city were trying to win. It's OK, Sawyer and Alison, cheer up."

Alison felt tears starting in her eyes. "I wanted to win that playground equipment so much," she thought. A tear trickled down her nose. She tried to tell Sawyer she was sorry, but her voice only cracked with sadness and disappointment.

Two days before summer vacation, Alison saw a note snaking across the room. It went from Sawyer to Paul to Charlie to Audrey and then to her. It was a page out of a magazine, folded into a smashed, little square. She unfolded it and read, "Kids! Win 4 tickets to the River City Water Park. Write Ricky Raccoon a birthday song!" And Sawyer had written across the bottom, "How about us two ex-losers trying again?" ◯

How did your thoughts or feelings change about Alison and Sawyer as the story went on? What events helped you change your thinking?

Stop and Respond

Sing It

Create a jingle about your own school or your favorite teacher. Use the melody of a well-known song or advertising jingle and change the words to fit your subject. Perform your jingle for the class.

Choose Your Words

Make a list of five words that capture the spirit of your school. Use a thesaurus and get creative! Draw a school banner using some of these words.

Write About It

In your journal, explain why Sawyer calls himself and Alison "ex-losers." Do you agree with this description? Why or why not?

What did you say?

by Carrie Waters

It costs an eye from the head?

Let's say you're visiting beautiful Madrid, Spain. You're having a great time. There's so much to see. You stroll past statues and fountains and beautiful parks. You turn down an avenue lined with stores. You drag your parents over to one of the stores to look in a window. There's a real matador's cape, just like the ones they use in the bullring!

"Wow," you wonder aloud, "how much does that cost?"

A man hears and waves his arms at you. "*Cuesta un ojo de la cara,*" he says.

What did he say? You look in your Spanish phrase book. Maybe you can afford that thing after all! *Cuestar:* to cost.

Cuesta un ojo de la cara: It costs an eye from the head.

It costs an eye from the head? Isn't that a *little* overpriced?

Was that guy kidding you or what?

The answer is, "or what." The man was using an **idiom.**

> The man's answer must be wrong. Or is it? Read on to see if you change your mind.

An idiom is a saying with a special meaning different from the meaning of the words in it. So *cuesta un ojo de la cara* means *it's very expensive!*

People use idioms all the time, without even thinking about it. Here in the U.S., we might say, *"It costs an arm and a leg."* Of course, nothing really does cost an arm and a leg. It's just another way of saying that something costs a lot!

Have you ever said, *"I'm so hungry I could eat a horse!"* If you have, you were using an idiom. You were saying that you were **very** hungry. You weren't really planning to eat a bronco or a palomino— not unless you have a really big overeating problem! You probably just had your eye on a seriously large BLT or something like that.

Hey, come to think of it, *had your eye on* is an idiom, too! Whew! They're everywhere.

had your eye on

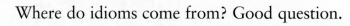

On the Flip Side

Where do idioms come from? Good question.

Some are fairly new. For example, *on the flip side* means the other side, or the opposite. It was first used when music was recorded on disks called records, instead of on tapes or CDs. Half the music was on each side of the record. So you had to flip a record over to the other side and replace it on the record player to hear all the music. Most idioms are much older than that. For example, to *have your ducks in a row* means to have everything just right. This saying comes from the way ducklings line up in a perfect row to follow a mother duck. Who first said it? No one knows. Most of us don't spend much time watching ducks these days. Still, we haven't outgrown the saying.

People who study language are always trying to retrace the history of idioms. They ask old-timers to recall how their grandparents used the sayings. They look through old newspapers and books and journals for clues. They discuss and argue. Maybe one explanation they find outdoes the others. But the origins of some of these sayings are lost forever. For example, no one knows for sure how we began using *okay,* even though we say it every day.

Have you ever used any of the following idioms?

Once in a blue moon has nothing to do with NASA or our space program. It means very rarely. When the moon was full twice in one month, the old *Farmer's Almanac* used blue ink to mark these times on its pages. You won't see a blue moon overhead very often!

Maybe you've heard some of these idioms before and thought you knew what they meant. How has this article changed your mind about their meanings?

Have you ever hit your elbow on something hard? The big bone from your shoulder to your elbow is called the *funny bone,* but believe me, striking it is not very funny! It's called a *funny bone* because the Latin name for it is *humerus.* Humorous. Funny. Get it?

To *bury the hatchet* means to put aside your differences or to declare peace. This idiom grew out of a Native American custom. When certain tribes agreed to be at peace and settle misunderstandings, they buried tomahawks as a symbol that they would fight no more.

goose bumps

Did you ever wonder why those little bumps you get on your arms when you're cold are called *goose bumps?* Well, at one time many farmers raised geese. Some of the farmers plucked the feathers off their geese five times a year. It's true! The feathers could be used on hats and in pillows and quilts. The skin of the geese looked dimpled without the feathers. *Goose bumps!* How attractive!

Now try this one: What idiom can you use to describe a scuba diver who is out of air? *In a pretty pickle* will do nicely. It means that you're in big trouble. This idiom comes from a Dutch saying that means "to sit in the salty liquid used for preserving pickles." *In a pretty pickle* is not a comfortable place to be!

Do you know what it means to *have something up your sleeve?* Hint: There's more than just an arm in there! This idiom originated in the 1400s, when clothing had no pockets. Where did people carry things? Tucked into their big, wide sleeves, that's where! When someone has *something up his sleeve,* watch out! He has a hidden scheme, or he is trying to mislead you.

Here's a wild one: *Round robin,* or doing something in turns, has nothing to do with a bird. *Robin* comes from *ruban,* a French word for ribbon. Back in the 1700s, it could be very dangerous to sign a petition to ask the king for anything. Apparently, kings were very touchy guys! If a petition made a king angry, he sometimes punished the person whose signature was at the very top. And we're talking beheading here! Since most people preferred their heads on their own shoulders, they began signing their names on a ribbon. Then they glued the ends of the ribbon together so the names formed a circle. Then no one's name was at the top!

Wow! When those kings *went bananas,* anyone who was *out of line* really had to *face the music,* huh? (Why not look these up yourself?)

Idioms. They are sprinkled all through our language. They make it more colorful and interesting. And new idioms continue to appear all the time. Who knows? Maybe you'll *coin one* yourself someday! ⬤

In a pretty pickle

Before you read this article, where did you think the expression "round robin" might have come from?

How many idioms do people in your class know? Check it out with this Idioms Quiz.

Idiom	What does it mean ?	Where did it come from?
Strike while the iron is hot.	Don't hesitate; choose the best time	Blacksmiths had to hit the iron with hammers while it was hot to shape new tools.
To take someone under your wing	Take care of that person or thing	Hens keep their chicks under their wings to protect them.
Get a break	Have things go well for you	In the game of pool, the first hit on all the balls is the "break." A good break puts the balls in good positions.
Fly off the handle	Get dangerously angry	Tools that flew off their handles were very dangerous.
On the nose	Exactly right	Directors of radio shows put their fingers on their noses to give the signal that the show was right on time.
Worth your salt	Worthy or worth your salary	Soldiers in ancient Rome were paid partly in salt.

Stop and Respond

y o _ _ ' r _ / p u l l i n _ / m _ / l _ _ _
Clue: "not being truthful"

Playing with Words

In a group of three or four students, play the following game. Each group member thinks of an idiom, such as *you're pulling my leg*. As you would in the game Hangman, write spaces for each letter of the phrase, using a slash (/) to separate each word. Below the spaces write a clue describing the subject of the idiom. For example, you might say "not being truthful" for the phrase above. Other group members take turns guessing letters or the idiom. Whoever guesses the idiom scores a point. The winner is the person with the highest score when the teacher calls "time."

Mix and Match

The article "What Did You Say?" has lots of information about where many idioms came from. Reread the article carefully, and then read the clues below. Each clue describes the source of the idiom. Find the idioms in the article that match the clues. We've done the first one for you.

petition signer = round robin
protective hens
disc jockeys
good workers
orderly quackers

Idioms From Around the World

Explore idioms from around the world. Work in a small group or with a partner. Pick a country and research an idiom from that culture. You might look in books, on the Internet, or ask a student who comes from that country for help. Share the idiom and its meaning with the class.

Let's Write

Say What You Mean

Words can have more than one meaning, and popular use of a word can change a lot over time. For instance, for many people, the word *gross* describes how much something weighs. People your age, however, use it to describe something disgusting. Look in a dictionary to find two different meanings for one of the following words: *blade, chill, disk, hip,* or *mouse.* Write two paragraphs that compare and contrast two different meanings of the word.

Words to Chew On

Tongue twisters are short phrases that are very difficult to say quickly. These twisty tidbits tangle our tongues terribly. Try saying "Unique New York" five times fast. Some people like to create their own tongue twisters. For example, a student from Richmond, VA, wrote this tidbit to describe his friend's involvement in the enrichment program at their school: *Richard's in Richmond's Enrichment.* Try your hand at writing your own tongue twister and share it with the class.

Fill in the Blanks

Write a 10-line story filled with lots of action or description. Go back to your story and erase the following: two nouns, two verbs, two adjectives, two adverbs, and at least one proper noun. Without sharing your story, ask a partner to give you one example of each part of speech. Then ask a second partner to give you their examples. Reread your story out loud to your partners, first with one set of words and then with the other. Discuss how word choice affects the outcome of a story.

More Books

Trussell-Cullen, Alan. *Playing with Words.* Shortland, 1996.

Jenkins, Gerald. *Be a Code Breaker.* Tarquin Publishers, 1997.

Funk, Charles Earle and Tom Funk. *2107 Curious Word Origins, Sayings, and Expressions from White Elephants to Song Dance.* Ingram Book Co., 1993.

On the Web

Merriam-Webster Word Games
http://www.m-w.com/game

More Word Games
http://www.funbrain.com

Famous Quotations
http://www.bartleby.com

What's in a First Name?
http://www.behindthename.com

Across the Curriculum

Social Studies

When you were born, your parents probably had several names picked out for you. Perhaps you might have been a Karen, but ended up a Laura instead. So what's in a name, anyway? Why do people agonize over what to name their children and even their pets? What does your name mean? Is it a family name passed down? Where did your name originate? Do some research on your name and create a poster to illustrate what you discover. Try looking in a book of baby names for information.

Fine Arts

Ever since people have been singing along with the radio, they have gotten the words to songs wrong. Even *The Star Spangled Banner* gets garbled! Sometimes music groups print the song's words, or *lyrics,* on the CD liner notes. Sometimes they don't. Listen to the radio for a popular song with unclear words. Ask five friends to sing or recite part of the song from memory. How many versions do you hear? Pick the funniest and share it with the class.

A Picture is worth a Thousand Words!

Sometimes you don't need words at all to get a message across. Around the world, signs are used to communicate important information to motorists and other travelers. No matter what language they speak, the meaning is clear. Or is it? What do you think the signs below mean?

Now it's your turn to design your own sign. Create a sign that would help a new non-English-speaking student find his or her way to an important place in your school.

COMPREHENSION QUARTERLY

4

CQ

ISSUE C: Synthesizing

99% DETERMINATION

99% Determination

THINK ABOUT: Synthesizing

C4

FICTION
Puppy Magic
Jenny comes up with a plan to convince her parents to let her have a dog.

C11

NONFICTION
Walking to Freedom
Read about where and why a VERY determined man named Anthony Cohen took a walk.

FICTION
The Show Must Go On!
How many things can go wrong when you try to put on a play? You might be surprised!

C19

C25

NONFICTION
Play Ball!
Do you like baseball? Read about two very determined teams.

SYNTHESIZING

A Very Special Competition

"Congratulations, Patty!" said Taneesha. She gave her neighbor a big hug. "I can't believe I know a gold medal winner!"

As she waved good-bye, Taneesha couldn't help but think of all the times she had seen Patty swimming laps in the local pool. Patty had been determined to do well in the Special Olympics. And she had!

Taneesha had been trying to decide on a nonfiction book to read for a school report. Now she decided that something about the Special Olympics would be perfect!

That afternoon, Taneesha opened the book she had found at the library. She remembered what her teacher had said about paying attention to text elements. She knew the headings were a clue about important points. So she made a note card for each heading. She also read the captions under the photographs and illustrations. And when she reached the end of the chapter, she read the summary very carefully.

By the time she finished, Taneesha was confident that she had **synthesized** the important information in the chapter and understood what she had read. She was now ready to go on to Chapter 2.

When reading, Taneesha has learned to look for elements of the text that will help her understand the meaning of what she reads. She surveys the text first to identify these elements. She pays attention to everything on the page—from photographs and captions to section headings.

History of Special Olympics
Started in 1968 by Eunice Shriver
Based idea on Olympic Games

Think about a book or article you have read recently. What text elements were most helpful to you?

Puppy M*A*G*I*C

by Claire Daniel

It had to be at least the twentieth time I had begged my parents to let me have a dog. As usual, my father listened to my arguments. But this time, instead of just saying no, he led me out to the back porch and pointed to our neighbor's four-month-old puppy, Magic.

"Look at that dog, Jenny. He chews up sneakers. He barks all the time. Now he's digging a hole next to the fence."

My dad was right. Magic was always getting into something.

"Puppies are a lot of trouble," he continued. "Besides that, who would feed him and train him and take him for walks every day? Your mother and I both work, and we don't have enough time as it is."

"I would!" I exclaimed. "I'd train him and take care of him. You and Mom wouldn't have to do anything. I promise!"

But Dad shook his head, went back inside, and said something to Mom. I knew they didn't think I could take care of a dog.

I was watching Magic drag an old bicycle tire across the yard when Mr. Wheeler came outside with a leash. When he tried to put the leash on, Magic started playing tug-of-war. I guess you could say that Magic "won" the game because he ran off, the leash in his mouth flailing wildly behind him. That was when the idea hit me: I would train Magic! Then my parents would *have* to see that I could take care of a pet!

With this plan in mind, I raced next door to see my neighbor. "Mr. Wheeler," I started to say, "could I train Magic for you?"

Mr. Wheeler laughed. "Magic is almost impossible to train!" As if to prove Mr. Wheeler's words, Magic headed straight for Mr. Wheeler, jumping on him and leaving muddy paw prints on his khaki pants.

"Couldn't I at least try? Say, for one hour a day?"

"Well, it certainly couldn't hurt to try," he agreed. "It's OK with me if it's OK with your parents."

Although my parents were unsure, they agreed. So that afternoon, I went to the library and checked out all the books I could find about dog training. I even found a video, but as I watched the video dog obey every command, I felt discouraged. Would Magic ever behave like that?

Who is telling this story? What do you know about her so far?

My first day of training was less than great. The books said that food rewards and praise would encourage a dog to obey. They also said that training a dog to come when it is called is very important. So, ready with a bag of dog biscuits, I commanded, "Magic, come!" Magic came toward me, sniffed the biscuit, and sat down. Excited by my success, I said, "Good boy," and gave him the biscuit. Magic gobbled it down . . . then jumped and knocked me over. Before I could get up, he had run off with the entire bag of dog biscuits. I chased him, trying to get the bag back from him, but Magic thought we were playing a game and led me on a wild chase around the backyard. If there had been a scorecard, it would have read: Magic 1, Jenny, 0.

That night I read the dog-training books more carefully. Magic was a smart dog. My job was to show him that I was smarter. I was determined that this dog was not going to get the best of me!

The next day, I called Magic to come to me. He came, and I gave him a biscuit. So far, so good. The next thing I did was what the books called the "alpha dog" routine. I pinned Magic down on the ground, covering him with my body so that he couldn't move. For a full minute, I held Magic there as he struggled to get free. Holding Magic in place taught him that I was the boss. Like the head dog in a dog pack, I let him know I was the "first," or "alpha" dog, and he had to obey me. Finally, he stopped struggling, and I let him go. The effect was amazing! He actually settled down.

The following day, I taught Magic to sit. As the dog-training books advised, I held a biscuit over his nose. Magic jumped for it, and I said, "No!" in a loud voice. I held it up again, and this time he just watched it. When I moved it over his head and toward his back, he sat down so he could see the biscuit. When he sat, I said, "Sit!" Then I gave him the biscuit. I did this a few times, and then just said, "Sit."

He sat. Good dog! I had just taught him his first command. I don't know who I was more pleased with—Magic or myself.

I worked with Magic every day. After 15 minutes of training, I played with him. I kicked and threw balls or played hide-and-seek. Sometimes we just ran around, hollering and barking (I hollered, he barked). For the last 15 minutes, I walked him on the leash in the park. This was not as much fun. Magic wanted to jump on joggers or chase bicycles. He wanted to eat everything. He was like a vacuum cleaner, gobbling everything in his path, from sandwiches to rocks to bottle caps.

I said "NO!" loudly whenever he did something wrong and "Good boy!" when he did things right. We developed our own routine, and soon I began to see big results. He started walking beside me in a "heel" position. He stopped jumping on people and chasing bicycles. He was great at fetching a ball. He could sit, stay, come, or wait on command.

After a month, I figured it was time to show my parents what I had done. So I leashed Magic and took him into the living room, where my dad and mom were quietly talking.

How does Jenny's account of training Magic help you get to know Jenny better?

"I have to show you what Magic can do!" I said, eager to begin the demonstration.

"Not now, Jenny. The Wheelers are coming over."

The doorbell rang, and the Wheelers came in. Magic knew something was going on, and he laid down on the floor beside me with a loud "Humph!"

"Jenny," Mr. Wheeler began, "we know how hard you've worked with Magic, and we want to thank you. However, we have a problem."

My heart sank. Hadn't I done a good job? I wanted them to know I needed more time, so I said, "But, Mr. Wheeler . . ."

He interrupted me. "You've done a fantastic job, and Magic is quite fond of you."

"Every night he goes to the window facing your house and whimpers," Mrs. Wheeler added.

"So what's wrong?" I asked.

"The problem is my wife and I are moving to the city in a month. We really love Magic and would love to keep him forever, but we think he'd be much happier with you than with us in our small apartment. We're hoping that you could keep Magic for us."

How does the dialogue on this page help you to know that the Wheelers are going to give Magic to Jenny?

Mom and Dad were smiling, and I knew they had already discussed it with the Wheelers. I looked down at Magic and saw his big brown eyes looking up into mine. I said, "I'll do it—on one condition." Grinning, I said, "You have to watch the 'Magic Dog Show,' so you can see what he's learned."

Everyone got comfortable so they could watch Magic perform. He sat, he stayed, and he even jumped through a hoop like a circus lion.

At one point, Mr. Wheeler laughed and said, "Can Magic multiply yet? Does he know Morse code?"

That was the moment Fluffy, our gray Persian cat, chose to strut through the living room. Magic barked, and the cat hissed and arched her back. With her hair sticking straight up on her back, Fluffy high-tailed it up the stairs with Magic following in hot pursuit.

"Well, I guess Magic still has a few more things to learn," I said sheepishly.

"That's OK, Jenny," said Mom. "We've got lots of time." ⬤

Stop and Respond

Problems Solved

Name one problem Jenny has at the beginning of "Puppy Magic" and one problem Magic's owner has. How does Jenny solve both problems at once? How does thinking about these problems and their solution help you better understand the story?

How Determined Are You?

Think about something you really, *really* want to have or want to do. Write a one-paragraph plan or make a list of steps that explains what you are willing to do to make your wish come true.

Training Manual

Draw a picture that shows a pet doing a trick. Then make a list of steps to train the animal to do that trick.

The Right Stuff

10

9

8

7

6

5

4

3

2

1

Perhaps you dream of someday being an astronaut and traveling into space. But do you have what it takes?

If you are determined to become an astronaut, you must

- **Have a good education.**
  It is especially important to do well in math and science. You will need these skills to do your job. Every astronaut must have also a college degree in math, science, or engineering.

- **Get along with other people.**
  If you travel into space, you will be living in a small area with other people for long periods of time. You'd better get along!

- **Be able to work as part of a team.**
  Astronauts depend on one another. If one person falls down on the job, everyone could be in danger.

- **Be physically fit.**
  Many of the jobs that astronauts do in space require endurance and strength. They have to be in great shape.

- **Meet certain physical requirements**
  Astronauts have to be between 4' 10 $\frac{1}{2}$" and 6' 4" tall. They can wear glasses as long as their vision isn't too bad.

So what can you do to get ready?

You can't do anything about your height or your vision. But you can do other things to get ready for astronaut training. (And guess what? These ideas will help you even if you decide on another career!)

- Take part in team sports or after-school clubs and organizations.

- Eat right and get into the exercise habit.

- Study hard. Get help if math and science aren't your best subjects.

- Learn another language so you can communicate with people from other countries.

WALKING TO FREEDOM

BY ADRIENNE B. LIEBERMAN

A MAN IN A BOX

On a steamy day in 1996, Anthony Cohen squeezed himself into a box. It measured 24 inches wide, 28 inches deep, and 30 inches high. Cohen and his friends had built a trapdoor so that he could get out, but no one could get in. They drilled air holes so he could breathe. So people could not peek in, they covered most of the air holes with stickers. Then Cohen's friends shipped him on a freight car from Philadelphia to New York City.

Inside the box, Cohen carried just a few things. He took a telephone, a bottle of water, a tiny quilt, a pillow, and a pocketknife.

The trip was supposed to take just two hours. But it took more than five. As the train left the station, Cohen peered through a tiny airhole. What he saw frightened him. The door of the freight car had begun to open. The terrified man watched as trees, cows, and farms flashed past. He feared that his box might fall out of the train and get smashed. And it hurt to sit still for so many hours. His legs were pressed painfully against his chest. He wondered whether the heat

would kill him. As it grew hotter inside the box, Cohen struggled to reach his knife. To cool off, he cut the legs off his pants.

Cohen's train finally reached New York City. But he almost kept going. His box had been mistakenly marked to travel even farther. Luckily, Cohen's friends found the box and pried him out. Sweat drenched his clothes. For hours, he gulped glass after glass of water.

ANOTHER DETERMINED MAN

What made Anthony Cohen climb into a box to take such a rough trip? Cohen, an African American historian, wanted to repeat the brave journey another African American had made about 150 years earlier in 1848. Henry "Box" Brown had also traveled by train in a tiny box. But he was fleeing from slavery to freedom.

Brown's 26 hour train ride from Richmond, Virginia, to Philadelphia, Pennsylvania, took more than five times as long as Cohen's. It was more uncomfortable, too. Railroad workers had ignored the warning on the box which read, "This side up. Handle with care." For hours, Brown crouched upside down. When he finally arrived in Philadelphia, people said he was "about as wet as if he had come up out of the Delaware." They gave him the nickname "Box" after this daring escape.

Fear and pain made Anthony Cohen want to quit before completing his own uncomfortable ride. But he kept himself going by thinking about Box Brown. He could keep going, Cohen told himself, because Box Brown had done it for 26 hours and succeeded.

How does the illustration on this page help you to better understand the difficulty of Cohen's journey?

RETRACING THE UNDERGROUND RAILROAD

Cohen's box adventure was just one part of a 6 week, 800 mile journey from Maryland to Canada. The historian had set out to follow one of the routes African Americans took to escape slavery. Most of these paths to freedom followed roads and rivers.

African American slaves called their freedom trails the "Underground Railroad," even though they did not travel underground and they rarely took trains. But to avoid being captured, the fleeing slaves had to travel at night and in secret. *Underground* is another word for "secret." They called the safe houses where they stayed *stations*. And the people who helped them, like Harriet Tubman, were called *conductors*.

Between the 1830s and the end of the Civil War in 1865, between 30,000 and 100,000 African Americans became passengers on the Underground Railroad to freedom. Anthony Cohen decided to travel in the very same ways these brave escapees had traveled. Sometimes he went by train or hitched a ride on a canal boat. But mostly, Cohen trudged by foot, mile after lonely mile.

FOURTH GRADERS INSPIRE A JOURNEY

How do the headings on pages C11–C13 help you to synthesize this part of the article?

The idea for this unusual journey came to Anthony Cohen in a classroom. The historian had been describing his library research on the Underground Railroad. The fourth-grade students asked multiple questions. They wondered if the escaping slaves got tired. How many miles could they walk in a day? Did they get scared?

Cohen knew a lot about the Underground Railroad, but he didn't know any of the answers to these questions. Not only that, but many of the stations on the Underground Railroad were still secret. To learn more about them and to discover how it might have felt to escape to freedom, Anthony Cohen decided to take a trip.

KEEPING A GOAL IN MIND

Cohen walked between 10 and 25 miles a day, mesmerizing school groups along the way when he spoke of his experiences. He continued to research possible Underground Railroad sites. He found one such site on a farm in western New York. He discovered a 12-by-15-foot room under a trapdoor in a barn. Soot on a wall and a hole in the ceiling made Cohen think a fireplace had once warmed the room.

The floor held smashed plates and rusted silverware. Cohen hoped that archaeologists— scientists who study the objects of the past—would later come back to study this site further.

Cohen did most of his traveling during the day so that he could do his research and speak to various groups at night. But to avoid capture by slave catchers, escaping African Americans had to travel by night. To understand their experiences, Cohen decided to spend one night on a path near the Erie Canal in western New York State. This path would eventually lead him to the Niagara River and Canada. Canada meant freedom to an escaping slave.

That rainy night, Cohen ran for 37 miles past swamps, fields, and even suburban houses. He was frightened when dogs chased him. When he felt like quitting, Cohen remembered the determination of the slaves who had made their way north to freedom. Cohen knew that these people would never have quit—they had no choice. Like Box Brown, they had risked their lives for the freedom we take for granted. So Cohen kept going.

Fifteen people met Anthony Cohen when he finally finished his trip to Canada. He was happy to see them but was even happier to have reached his goal. Falling to his knees, Cohen plunged his hands into the Canadian dirt. Then he wept tears of joy.

How does the use of numbers in this section of the article help you to understand the difficulties that escaping slaves faced?

STILL WALKING

Two years later, Anthony Cohen decided to trace a different route of the Underground Railroad. This time, he would travel from the Deep South to Canada. Cohen began this journey in Mobile, Alabama.

After walking through large parts of seven states, he wrote to the people who traced his daily progress on the Internet: "This is challenging work, but it is the closest thing to what the slaves did."

What was the best part? Many people along Cohen's path knew about his second trip. They cheered him on. Cohen wrote: "Walking through Ohio at night, I have seen many homes with lanterns or candles in the window—the old sign identifying an Underground Railroad station. And on a clear night, I can look skyward and see the same sky that the slaves saw."

So the next time you think you are tired of walking, take a minute to think about Anthony Cohen and all those brave men and women who walked before him. ◉

Stop and Respond

KEEP ON GOING

Anthony Cohen says that when he wanted to give up, remembering the slaves kept him going. Write a paragraph that explains what keeps you going when you are tempted to give up.

THE SAME AND DIFFERENT

What are two ways that Anthony Cohen's walks are similar to the journeys of a slave on the Underground Railroad? What are two ways that they are different? How does making these comparisons help you understand the meaning of the article?

FEELINGS ABOUT FREEDOM

Write a rhymed or unrhymed poem that describes your feelings about being a free person. Add an illustration or border to your work.

The Never-Give-Up Awards

Lou Gehrig

Stevie Wonder

Susan B. Anthony

Each of the people described below is a winner of a Never-Give-Up Award because of his or her determination. Can you match the descriptions to the names?

1. She broke the law by casting a vote in a presidential election. Her determination helped to win women the right to vote.

2. Her parents wanted her to give up track and field because they didn't think it was a good sport for a girl. But she kept on competing and eventually won many Olympic gold medals.

3. This scientist wrote a book that made people realize that DDT was a chemical that harmed humans and animals.

4. Although he was totally blind, this young boy spent four years adapting a military code into an alphabet a blind person could use to read and write.

5. It was against the law to teach a slave to read and write. So this boy spent seven years teaching himself. He became an Abolitionist—a person who works to end slavery—and wrote a book about the evils of slavery.

6. This New York Yankee never missed a game—even when he had broken fingers. After he came down with a terrible disease, he still came to games and sat with his teammates.

7. Despite his deafness, this musician kept composing. He had the legs sawed off his piano so he could put it on the floor to feel the vibrations.

8. Born blind, this boy worked hard to develop his own musical talents. He was a singing star by the time he was a teenager.

Lou Gehrig

Frederick Douglass

Stevie Wonder

Susan B. Anthony

Ludwig van Beethoven

Rachel Carson

Jackie Joyner Kersee

Louis Braille

Rachel Carson

SYNTHESIZING

Flights of Inspiration

Inez's class was studying the history of flight. Her teacher gave her a book called *The Road to Kitty Hawk*. Inez read the first chapter, but she was having trouble keeping all the information straight.

"Look for text elements that will help you understand what you're reading," Ms. Gomez suggested. "Things like charts, photos, time elements. She noticed an interesting time line. It showed her that people had been experimenting with flying and flying machines for hundreds of years before the Wright brothers' successful flight.

She went on to reread the summary at the end of the first chapter. "I see what Ms. Gomez means," she said to herself. "This

Early Experiments and Gliding

German engineer Otto Lilienthal made more than 2,500 successful manned glider flights in the early 1890s. His writings about airplane design greatly influenced and inspired the Wright brothers.

The History of Flight

350 BC
Chinese build the first kites

1804
Sir George Cayley builds the first successful glider

1903
Wright brothers build and fly the world's first successful airplane in Kitty Hawk, NC

400 BC
Greek scholar builds a wooden pigeon that moves through the air

1500 AD
Leonardo da Vinci draws flying machines

1891
Otto Lilienthal makes the first successful manned glider flight

lines, and chapter summaries." The teacher pointed to a photograph. "For example, what does this tell you?" she asked.

Inez looked at the picture, which showed a man wearing a strange winglike contraption. She read the caption underneath. "This guy tried to fly before the Wright brothers did," she said. "It says he inspired them."

Inez took the book back to her desk. She turned pages, looking for other text

summary talks about all the important stuff in the chapter."

Inez realizes that focusing on text elements will help her **synthesize** everything she's read so that she can better understand her topic. As she reads the next chapter, she will remember to pay attention to the text elements.

Think about a book you have read recently. Did the text elements increase your understanding of what you read?

THE SHOW MUST GO ON

By Cynthia Mercati

The Characters:

ANNIE, stage manager

MARIA, prompter

LUKE

ERICA

NATE

MAX

GREG

MARNIE, Dorothy

MR. RODRIQUEZ, teacher/director

CHRISSY, lion

The Scene: *Backstage, at a fourth grade presentation of* The Wizard Of Oz.

Facing upstage and toward the pretend audience are several flats, or walls. The "real" audience will see only the back of these. There is also a table on which the props and a large boom box are set. MARIA sits on a high stool, a script in her hand. ANNIE, LUKE, ERICA, NATE, GREG, and MAX are gathered together. They're all excited and a little jittery, too. This is opening night.

ERICA: I hope we're ready.

ANNIE: I was up until midnight last night worrying about things!

NATE: Calm down!

GREG: I built this scenery with my own two hands. It's solid as a rock.

(As he thumps his fist on a flat, he knocks a preset hole in it.)

NATE: Uh-oh.

GREG: All I did was put my knuckles like this—

ANNIE: Don't do it again!

GREG: I'm sorry! I'm really sorry! I'm really, really sorry! I'm—

ERICA: We get it. You're sorry.

GREG: I'm really, really, really sorry!

ANNIE: It's OK, Greg, we know you didn't mean to do it.

(MARNIE, *dressed as Dorothy and carrying a stuffed Toto, pokes her head in the large hole* GREG'S *fist has left in the flat.*)

MARNIE: It's not OK. My play is ruined!

NATE: *Your* play?

MARNIE: Dorothy's the lead role, and I'm playing Dorothy.

LUKE: You know what Mr. Rodriquez said. Every part is just as important as every other part.

ANNIE: And the backstage people are just as important as the actors.

ERICA: And we all have to work together to put this play on!

MARNIE: Tell it to my agent! Well, when I get an agent, you can tell it to him.

NATE: Forget your agent. What are we gonna do about the set?

GREG: Cancel the show, I guess.

ANNIE: No way!

MARIA: I've got an idea, Annie. *(Starts to run offstage.)* Back in a flash!

ANNIE: We'd better make sure everything else is working OK. Let's give the sound effects a quick run-through.

MAX *(as he dashes over to the boom box):* Whatever you say, Annie—you're the stage manager!

ANNIE *(looking at her script):* Cue Toto's bark!

MAX: Yes, sir! Uh—yes, ma'am! *(He pushes a button, but nothing happens.)* I must've pushed the wrong button. *(He pushes all the buttons, getting more and more excited. Finally, he yanks the tape out.)* The tape is probably just jammed. I can fix it!

ERICA: Be careful, Max!

MAX: Careful is my middle name! *(While he is saying this, he pokes at the tape—and it completely unravels. This should be preset.)* Uh-oh.

MARNIE: How can we have a show with a barkless Toto?

GREG: It's curtains! I mean, it's curtains even before we get the curtain up! We'll have to cancel.

ANNIE AND LUKE: No way!

NATE: We could say Toto has a cold and lost his voice.

> How does the dialogue format of a play help you to synthesize the content of the story? What differences do you notice between reading a play and a story with a narrative format?

MAX: I've got an idea. I've got a great bass voice! *(And he gives a good imitation of a dog's bark.)*

ERICA: You sound just like my cocker spaniel!

MAX: I can bark for Toto! *(MAX gives a few more barks, really getting into it.)* Maybe I should play Toto myself! *(He demonstrates.)* I can roll over—and sit up and beg!

NATE: Down, Lassie!

MARNIE: You'd better be good, Max—I don't want anything to ruin my play! *(MARNIE exits as MARIA enters, carrying a large posterboard.)*

MARIA *(indicating the poster):* We can put this over the hole!

LUKE *(reading):* HOLE IN THE WALL DUE TO ANGRY SOW.

ANNIE: It's exactly right for Dorothy's farmhouse!

MAX: You're our knight in shining armor, Maria!

MARIA: I'll go put it up. *(She exits to put the posterboard over the hole in the flat. She then joins the others.)*

ANNIE: Maria's done more work on this show than anyone. She's painted and sewed—and been the prompter at every rehearsal.

ERICA: She wanted to read for the part of Dorothy, but at the last minute, she got scared.

ANNIE *(a sudden thought):* Uh-oh.

NATE: What?

ANNIE: We don't have the sound for the tornado anymore—it was on the tape, too!

GREG: If we don't have a tornado, how is Dorothy going to get to Oz?

GREG: We'll have to cancel!

WHOOSH!

ANNIE, LUKE, ERICA *(yelling):* No way!

LUKE: We can flick the lights on and off.

GREG: But we still won't have the sound!

ANNIE: Oh, yes we will! *(She grabs a large black piece of material from the prop table.)* I'm going to tear this into three pieces! *(She tears the material into three preset pieces.)*

ERICA: That was for the witch's castle!

ANNIE: I know, but when the going gets tough, the tough get creative! *(She hands a piece of material to ERICA, MAX, and GREG.)* Put these on! *(The three drape the material around them, as ANNIE gestures to them.)* You're going to be the tornado!

ERICA, GREG, MAX: Huh?

ANNIE: It'll be like a dance! *(Standing in place, she waves her arms and bends her knees, demonstrating.)* Just pretend you're the wind—kneel down, go underneath each other—bow your legs out! Make whooshing sounds!

ERICA, GREG, MAX: Huh?

MARIA: I get it, Annie! *(She turns to the other three.)* I'll show you how to do it! First, you have to hold hands! *(The three join hands.)* Now do exactly what I do! *(MARIA weaves her way around the room, making whooshing and swishing noises as she spins and dips. The other three, still holding hands, follow after her. Awkwardly at first, then with growing confidence, they copy her movements.)*

LUKE *(watching the four move around the room):* That *does* kind of look like a tornado.

GREG *(all excited):* I'm gonna be on stage! I'm gonna be in front of the audience! *(Suddenly, he grabs his stomach.)* I'm gonna be sick. I feel like a hundred butterflies are gnawing away at my stomach!

LUKE: You've got stage fright!

GREG: I hope I live until the show!

ANNIE: We'd better check the props. *(NATE and ERICA go to the prop table.)* Dorothy's basket.

NATE *(holding it up):* Check!

ANNIE: Glinda's wand!

ERICA *(holding it up):* Check!

ANNIE: The ruby slippers!

NATE: Uh-oh.

ANNIE: Where are the ruby slippers?

ERICA: Don't panic, guys! I took the ruby slippers home last night to keep them safe and sound!

LUKE: So where are they?

ERICA *(brightly):* They're at home—safe and sound. *(Realizing what she's done, she shouts it out.)* They're at home!

ANNIE: The show is on in eight minutes!

GREG: We'll have to cancel!

ANNIE, LUKE, ERICA, MARIA: No way!

LUKE: We don't really need slippers! All we need are red shoes. And I know just where we can find some. Greg, take off your shoes!

GREG: I've got a hole in my sock!

NATE: That's show biz!

LUKE *(pointing to the shoes GREG is taking off):* I give you the ruby high-tops!

How does the dialogue between the characters help you get to know them better?

NATE: That's much cooler than those silly high heels. *(Demonstrating, he does the moon walk.)* Now Dorothy can *really* get around Oz!

ANNIE *(slumping down on the stool):* I can't think of one more thing that could go wrong.

(MARNIE and MR. RODRIQUEZ enter. MARNIE has obvious red splotches on her face.)

MARNIE: I can! Look at me! I've got hives! Mr. Rodriquez called the doctor and it turns out I'm allergic to stage makeup.

MR. RODRIQUEZ: We'll have to cancel the play!

ANNIE, LUKE, ERICA, MARIA, MAX, NATE: No way!

ANNIE: I know you're the director and our teacher, Mr. Rodriquez, but we just can't

give up now! We've been working for weeks on this show! We made the costumes . . .

MARIA: And built the set . . .

LUKE: And painted it . . .

ERICA: And found the props!

NATE: The cast learned their lines . . .

MAX: And practiced every day after school!

ANNIE: And tonight we've had one emergency after another!

LUKE: A hole in the flat . . .

ERICA: We lost Toto's bark . . .

MAX: And the tornado . . .

NATE: And the ruby slippers!

LUKE: But we solved every problem!

ERICA: We didn't give up!

ANNIE: And we're not going to give up now! We're going to put this show on!

GREG, MR. RODRIQUEZ: How?

ANNIE: Maria can play Dorothy—she knows the script better than anyone!

MR. RODRIQUEZ (the light dawning): Of course she does. She's the prompter.

GREG: But does she know Dorothy's part?

ANNIE: Forward and backward!

MARIA (surprised): How did you know?

ANNIE: I've seen you at rehearsal. Whenever Marnie forgets a line, you don't have to look at the script to give it to her. You've got the part down cold!

MR. RODRIQUEZ: Do you think you can do it, Maria?

MARIA: Well . . .

MARNIE: Of course she can! (Speaks right to Maria.) You'll be great, Maria! (She grabs MARIA'S hand and starts pulling her offstage.) Come on, you've got to get into this costume!

NATE: Hey, Marnie, what happened to *your* play?

MARNIE: Hearing you guys talk, I realized it was *our* play! I'm just as determined as the rest of you to make sure it goes on! (She runs off with MARIA.)

> How does the use of italics for stage directions help you to focus on the action of the play?

NICK: (calling after the girls): Remember, Maria—you're going out there a prompter, but you're coming back a star!

ANNIE: Wow, we did it—we really did it! Or I mean, we're about to do it!

(CHRISSY, dressed as the lion, rushes in, all in a panic.)

CHRISSY: I can't find my tail!

THE OTHERS: Uh-oh!

The End

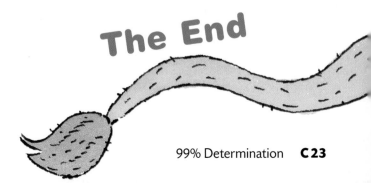

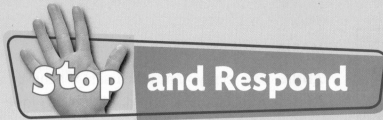

Stop and Respond

Problems and Solutions

List four problems the students in the cast had and the solution they found for each. Which solution do you think was the most creative? What is one other way to solve the same problem?

Knock. Knock. Knock.

Come One, Come All!

Create a playbill for the play. Fold a sheet of unlined paper in half to make a booklet. Include the title of the production, a list of characters, and information about the backstage crew. Don't forget an illustration for the cover!

Sound Effects

Imagine that you are in charge of sound effects for a play. What would you use to create each of the following sounds?

gentle rain   **thunder**   **doorbell**
fire siren   **hailstorm**   **running feet**

Play Ball!

by Gail B. Riley

"Don't think it's impossible to get here. Because that's what we thought, and we got here." Those are the words of twelve-year-old Ross Haggard describing the success of his Texas team, the Bellaire Little League All-Stars. All season long, the All-Stars had been a model of determination and hard work. They had practiced long and hard and had played their very best against their opponents. And now their determination and hard work had led them to what had only been a dream—to play in the first Little League World Series of the new millennium.

Coach Terry McConn said, "In the Little League World Series final game, our guys were the most focused group of twelve-year-olds you ever saw, and that's what got them there. My coaching and their ability isn't what made the difference—it was their way of focusing and preparing mentally for every game, and they played their hearts out."

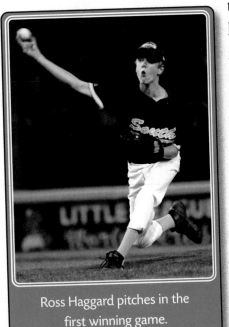

Ross Haggard pitches in the first winning game.

The All-Stars had never even won a district title before the Little League World Series. But the team won game after game to capture the district title—and then had kept on winning. In the final round of U.S. championship play, All-Stars pitcher Ross Haggard showed his power, the result of many long hours of practice. Haggard had a true knack for pitching. He had already thrown a no-hitter in one earlier game, and had struck out 12 players in another. Such play was amazing for someone who had broken his wrist in a snowboarding accident just months before! Yet Haggard had undertaken the task of getting his wrist back in shape and had met his goal. Now in the critical championship game, Haggard threw a four-hitter, striking out 13 players to catapult his team to the championship. "It felt really good," Haggard said. "I mean, winning the U.S. championship! That's awesome!"

A view of the playing field from the hilltop.

But the All-Stars' work was far from over. All summer, they continued to practice long and hard in anticipation of the Little League World Series. Before they knew it, summer had melted away, and the team was on its way to Williamsport, Pennsylvania, for the championship game. When they arrived at the ballpark, they stared down from the top of a grassy hill to the neatly-trimmed turf of the playing field. In just a matter of days, the All-Stars knew, they would be racing around that manicured diamond and covering all parts of that field. Their friends and family would sit in this very spot to watch them play. It sent shivers down their spines just thinking of it.

Soon after the players arrived in Williamsport, television cameras, reporters, and celebrities followed. Telephones jangled as reporters set up stories and the players gave interviews and press conferences. As they went onto the field, the All-Stars knew this game would be an experience like no other. Hall of Fame member George Brett and actor Kevin Costner tossed out the first two pitches. It was time to play ball!

In this contest for the world title, the All-Stars faced a Venezuelan team, Sierra Maestra-Maracaibo. The journey through Little League games in South America to the championship diamond in the United States had been equally challenging for Sierra Maestra-Maracaibo. For starters, the team's home practice field looked more like a road under construction than a baseball field. Dozens of holes covered the field's surface. And the team owned only one bat—one that was dented and scuffed! "It was all we could afford," said team manager Eduvino Quevedo. "And without it, we could never have played for the title." But these obstacles did not stop the team from working toward its goal—to play in the Little League championship game.

The author included a photograph of the playing field described by the All-Stars. How does this help you to understand what the All-Stars were feeling?

After winning the local title, the Venezuelan players boarded a plane for the United States. Despite mechanical problems that caused the plane to turn back, the team's spirits were high. "This team has a bunch of fighters," said manager Quevedo. "They don't give up very easily."

Once in the United States, equipment companies donated new bats to Sierra Maestra-Maracaibo. The team marveled at the fine quality of the new bats. They were ready to play. The Venezuelan players showed their determination on the field as well as at the plate. Pitcher Ruben Mavarez had a know-how all his own when it came to getting the ball over the plate, and he had practiced hard to master his curveball. Although his hard work was to pay off again and again, it was hard not to get discouraged when his team lost the first game of the Series to Tokyo by 10–0. But once again, the team pushed forward, determined to overcome the obstacles in their path.

Now the All-Stars and Sierra Maestra-Maracaibo were facing each other in the

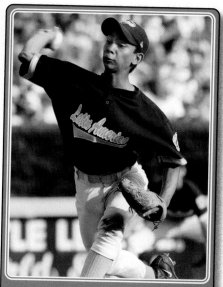
Mavarez pitches for Venezuela.

Mavarez flashes a victory sign after the World Series win.

final game of the Little League World Championship. Forty-two thousand people packed the stands, cheering wildly for their team throughout the game. Back home, the friends and families of both teams huddled around their television sets, some holding their breath, others gnawing their fingernails. Both teams played hard and well throughout the game. Both fought hard for the championship. But in the final inning, Venezuela's pitcher, Ruben Mavarez, stretched back, then hurled his famous fastball. In the next instant, the final game of the Little League World Series was over. Mavarez had struck out the batter, bringing the final score to 3-2. Venezuela had captured the first Little League World Championship of the millennium!

Ruben Mavarez tossed his glove into the air and fell to his knees. His teammates rushed over to congratulate their pitcher. "It feels good to be a champion," said Mavarez. "I had a lot of faith in my teammates . . . My first thought when it was over was that I got the win. Then I thought of my country and my family . . . It's a big event in my life." Team members on both sides shed a few

Both teams race across the field after the World Series.

tears. Some were tears of happiness. Others were tears of sadness.

After the game, the All-Stars dashed across the field to help the Venezuelan team carry their championship banner. Only one team could win the Little League World Series title, but both teams went home feeling like champions. As All-Stars pitcher Ross Haggard said, "It was tough to take at first, but then we realized it was pretty good just to be the U.S. champs."

Back home after the Series, the All-Stars found themselves honored almost everywhere they went. They rolled down the streets of Bellaire and Houston in two parades. And they were honored by fans at a Houston Astros baseball game.

> How do the quotes from the coaches and players affect your synthesis of this article?

They even received a letter from George W. Bush who was then the governor of Texas. In his letter, he wrote, "Determination and teamwork represent the spirit of Texas. I commend you for your hard work and dedication. You make the Bellaire community and the Lone Star State proud."

What does the future hold for the Bellaire All-Stars and the Venezuelan Sierra Maestra-Maracaibo? Only time will tell. But one thing is certain. Both teams showed the world what can be accomplished by hard work and determination. And because of that, members of both teams are already winners in a very big way. ○

> What effect do the photographs in the article have on your synthesis of the content?

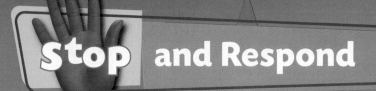

Rah! Rah!

Pick one team and write a funny or inspiring cheer for its members.

Collector's Card

Make a baseball card featuring Ross Haggard or Ruben Mavarez. On one side, draw a picture of the player. On the other side, record the name of his team, his position, and interesting facts about him.

Interview Time

With a partner, list four questions that a newspaper reporter might ask in an interview with a player or coach in the Little League World Series. Then role-play the interview with one of you taking the role of the coach or player and the other the role of the reporter.

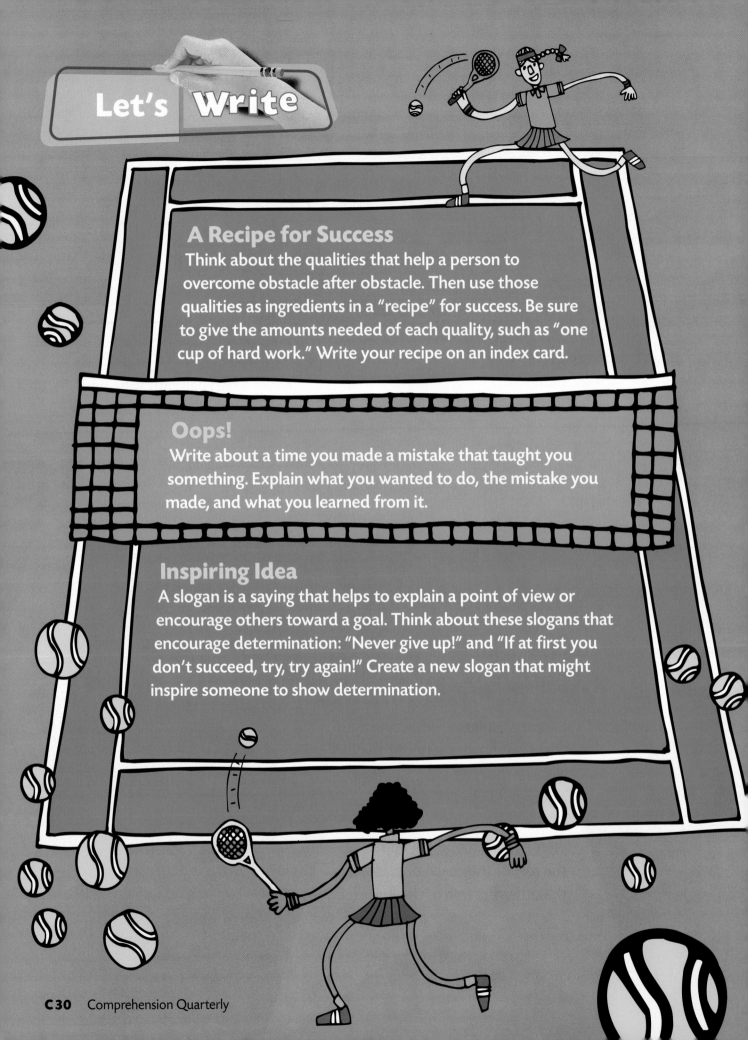

A Recipe for Success

Think about the qualities that help a person to overcome obstacle after obstacle. Then use those qualities as ingredients in a "recipe" for success. Be sure to give the amounts needed of each quality, such as "one cup of hard work." Write your recipe on an index card.

Oops!

Write about a time you made a mistake that taught you something. Explain what you wanted to do, the mistake you made, and what you learned from it.

Inspiring Idea

A slogan is a saying that helps to explain a point of view or encourage others toward a goal. Think about these slogans that encourage determination: "Never give up!" and "If at first you don't succeed, try, try again!" Create a new slogan that might inspire someone to show determination.

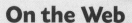

More Books

Burnford, Sheila. *The Incredible Journey.* Dell, 1996.

Christopher, Matt. *Olympic Dream, Vol. 47.* Little, Brown, 1996.

Naylor, Phyllis Reynolds. *The Fear Place.* Macmillan, 1994.

Reeder, Carolyn. *Captain Kate.* Morrow, 1999.

Taylor, Theodore. *The Cay.* Doubleday, 1987.

Verheyden-Hilliard, Mary E. *Scientist with Determination, Elma Gonzalez.* Equity Institute, 1985.

Perry, Armstrong. *Call It Courage.* Macmillan, 1940.

On the Web

Thirty Years of Heroes (Special Olympics)
http://www.snsgraphics.com/so_anv30/
heroes9/heroes.htm

So You Want to Be an Astronaut?
http://www.pbs.org/kcet/johnglenn/
justforkids/astronaut/index.htm

Do You Have What It Takes to Become a Firefighter?
http://www.pbs.org/testofcourage/
life1.html

Across the Curriculum

Research
Find out about an athlete, scientist, or leader who accomplished something important because he or she refused to give up. Give a short oral report about the obstacles the person had to overcome to reach his or her goal.

Debate
Should kids be discouraged from spending too much time playing competitive sports? Consider the question: How much competition is too much? Choose a point of view. Then list statements to support that viewpoint. Compare your arguments with those of a classmate.

Poster Art
Create an inspirational poster that would encourage its readers to keep on trying when they encounter problems while working toward a goal.

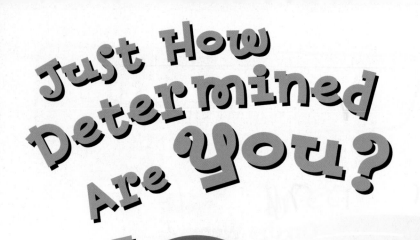

Just How Determined Are You?

Take this quiz to find out just how determined you are.

Imagine that you are trying to learn something new, like ballet, juggling, or in-line skating. Read each of the sentences below. Then think about how well each description fits you.

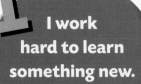

1

I work hard to learn something new.

Very Much   Somewhat
Not at All

2

I am willing to keep on working even when others give up.

Very Much   Somewhat
Not at All

3

I work at something for as long as it takes.

Very Much   Somewhat
Not at All

5

I learn something from my mistakes.

Very Much   Somewhat
Not at All

4

I don't get upset when I make mistakes.

Very Much   Somewhat
Not at All

The more you answered Very Much, the more determined you are!

COMPREHENSION QUARTERLY

CQ

4

ISSUE D: Inferring

Zoom In

Zoom In

THINK ABOUT: Inferring

D4

FICTION
A Closer Look
Is Jackie's overactive imagination in high gear? Or has something really happened to Andrew?

D11

NONFICTION
Meet Georgienne Bradley, Underwater Photographer
Swim with sharks? There's nothing this photographer would rather do.

FICTION
Once and for All
Who's the best? Maggie and Hank need an out-of-this-world experience to answer this question.

D19

D25

NONFICTION
Game Kids
Can you do more than play? Yes, be a winner— design a computer game!

In this issue:

INFERRING

Beyond Words

Charlie and Sam are best friends. Like most of the kids in the neighborhood, they like sports and spend hours on computer games. But the two spend even more time reading—usually science fiction, their favorite genre. They like to read the same book at the same time so they can discuss it as they read. This week, they are reading the first chapter of a book by one of their favorite authors and are comparing their reactions. The last paragraph of this chapter is below.

"That's it!" muttered Alevia under her breath. "I've practiced my whole life for this moment, and I've got to take a chance." The young Borglenian tucked her passport chip into its slot behind her ear, stepped into her pod, and input the numbers she'd found in Pangolin's journal. With a tiny *whhrrr* and a quick flash, Alevia was gone—from Borglene, anyway.

"I never thought that she'd have the nerve to take off like that," said Charlie. "She's been saying such cautious things in this chapter— like she'd never do anything to upset her parents."

"Yes, but she did stand up to that bully, Carmean," replied Sam thoughtfully. "People sometimes say one thing, but their actions tell you something else about them. I predict she'll do something even braver later in the book. What do you think?" The two pals continued talking about the first chapter for a few minutes.

Think about a time you and another person differed in your views about something you read. Both of you had used what you read and your own experiences to make different **inferences.** Often, careful readers make inferences to help draw conclusions and make predictions. Inferences often lead to predictions, and readers can check and change their predictions as they make their way through the text. People can have different inferences, but that's OK, as long as their inferences are based on evidence they've gathered from their reading.

A Closer Look

by Beth Raisner Glass

"One of these days, Jacqueline B. Torres, if you're not careful, you're going to get into real trouble," Jackie told herself as she looked in the mirror. Seeing her image before her, Jackie sighed. With crutches under her arms, a wheelchair behind her, and one leg trapped in a very stiff cast, her condition would make any typical ten-year-old just about give up. But Jackie was not typical.

Jackie sat back in her wheelchair and rolled herself to the bedroom window. All the while, she was thinking of her accident last month in her neighbor Andrew's treehouse. "I bet you can't climb up to the highest branch with one arm tied behind your back!" Andrew had challenged.

"I think I can," Jackie had contradicted. People who knew Jackie understood that she never backed down from any challenge. "This little tree can't be more than ten feet high," Jackie had added.

"Uh, yeah," Andrew had replied. "My dad and I measured it last week. So go ahead. What are you waiting for?" Andrew dared her.

And so Jackie had begun her trek to the top. With each step, branches fell from beneath her feet.

As Jackie recalled her struggle, she broke out in a sweat. Still, sitting in her wheelchair and looking out at the tree that had betrayed her, Jackie smiled. She was proud of herself for even trying. "Just because the tree was slippery, *and* the branches were the skinniest ever, *and* I fell and broke my leg doesn't mean I couldn't have made it to the top. I just didn't . . . this time," she said aloud, thinking she had no audience.

"Oh really?" A voice startled Jackie.

Jackie spun from the window. "Andrew! What are you doing here?"

"Just checking in on the patient. How are you? Enjoying the view?" he teased. "Those leaves on our tree should be turning colors by now."

Jackie's face turned bright red. "Hmph," was all she could muster.

Just then, they both heard a loud noise coming from Andrew's garage. Jackie and Andrew looked out the window. It was hard to see clearly through their tree. But only Jackie's face wrinkled with concern.

"What do you think that is, Andrew? It's coming from your garage. Wait! Sssh . . . I'll bet it's a . . ."

"Oh, forget it, Jackie. You're always imagining things. It's probably nothing. Here." Andrew shoved a magazine at Jackie. "I brought this for you. You can read it while you're cooped up in here," he said, smiling. Jackie slowly turned from the window, but she barely looked at the magazine cover. If she had really seen it, surely the issue *Trees Anyone Can Climb* would be flying across the room.

"Bye!" Andrew called, laughing.

Night was falling as Andrew ran across the yard back to his house. Waving up at Jackie, he covered his mouth and pointed to his garage in jest.

> What kind of person do you think Jackie is? What information in the text did you use to come to this conclusion?

Jackie rolled her eyes and threw back her hair in disgust.

That night, instead of watching her favorite television show, "Deceptions of the Universe," Jackie began constructing a telescope. First she wanted to solve her own mystery.

"I need a closer look," she said aloud. "I've got to find out what's going on in Andrew's garage. I can't be sure, but it sounded pretty strange, like something heavy being rolled around by someone—or some*thing!*"

When Jackie looked out her window later that night, she had her telescope ready to go. Crafted from a paper towel roll with cellophane wrap pulled taut in the front and a magnifying glass glued to the end, it was nearly perfect. Jackie leaned toward the window for a closer look. "Oh no," she groaned. "Even with a full moon, it's hard to see out there." Jackie rolled across her room and fumbled in the darkness for a flashlight. When she found it, she strapped it onto her telescope with an elastic band and tried again. To her horror, Jackie saw what looked like three heads outside of Andrew's garage. But that wasn't all. Near the heads on the driveway was a lone sneaker! Jackie needed a better look. But she couldn't move. Her wheelchair would make too much noise and she'd wake her parents if she tried to go down the hall to another window. "It'll have to wait until morning light," Jackie decided.

"I'll be able to see more clearly then, I'm sure."

After little sleep, Jackie found morning frost covering her viewing window. It added another dimension to her view of Andrew's garage. This time when

What do you think is happening in Andrew's garage? Why do you think that?

Jackie looked outside, the three heads looked as though they were floating! The sneaker remained where it was— and it was Andrew's! Jackie quickly grabbed the phone and dialed Andrew's number. "Hello? Hello? Is Andrew there?" Jackie managed to get out.

"Why hello, Jackie," answered Andrew's father, sounding nervous. "No, Andrew went . . . a . . . away for a few days. Bye now." *Click*. The line went dead.

All the color drained from Jackie's face. She was now whiter than a sheet. "It's a good thing I get my cast off today," she thought. "I've got to get over to Andrew's garage!"

Later that day, Jackie was in her room exercising her leg, which had just been freed from the cast. There was a knock at the door. "Who is it? Andrew, is it you? Come in! Come in!" Jackie called, excitedly.

"Hi, hon." It was Jackie's father. "I'd like you to see something. Please come with me."

Jackie wondered if her dad had seen what she saw, but she didn't dare ask. "He'll just think I'm wrong, but I know what I saw—three heads and Andrew's sneaker," she thought, following her father out the back door and then across the yard. "Why is he taking me to Andrew's house? Does he suspect something, too?" she wondered.

"Just a few more steps and we'll be there," urged her father. "Oh no! I forgot something at home. I'll be right back."

What do you think will happen next? Why do you think so?

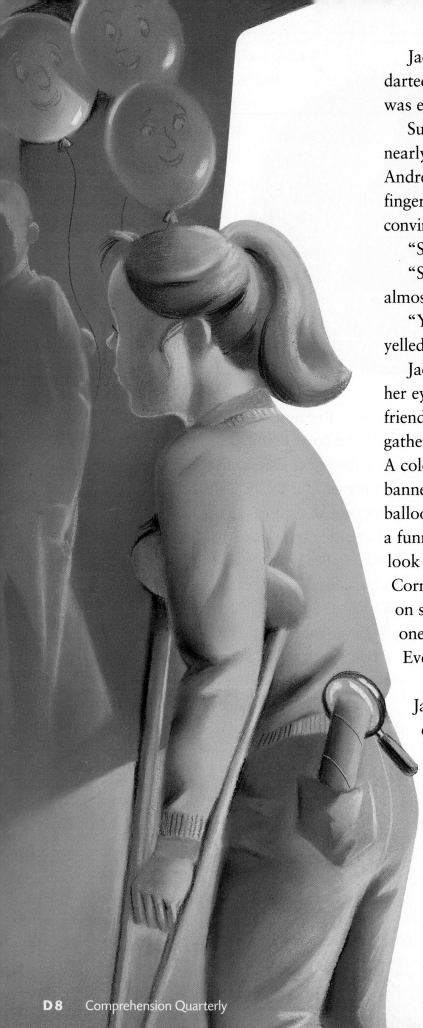

Jackie knocked at Andrew's door. Her eyes darted wildly around the yard. Everything was empty and silent.

Suddenly, the door swung open. Jackie nearly fell over. Standing in the doorway was Andrew's dad motioning to her. He placed his finger over his lips. Quietly, Jackie entered, convinced she would see Andrew's body inside.

"SURPRISE!"

"Sur–pr–ise?" Jackie asked, confused. She almost fell onto Andrew.

"Yes! Surprise!" everyone yelled again.

Jackie couldn't believe her eyes. A crowd of her friends and neighbors were gathered together in her honor. A colorful "Congratulations!" banner hung from the ceiling. Three giant balloons were suspended in the air, each with a funny face drawn on it. Scarecrows made to look like every guest decorated the room. Cornstalks and pumpkins were centerpieces on snack tables. Then Jackie noticed that no one was wearing a left shoe. She laughed. Everyone was using a crutch—just like her!

"This is the best get-well party ever!" Jackie said, grinning. She nudged Andrew, exclaiming, "I never would have guessed *this!*"

"What did you think was going on, Jackie?" Andrew teased.

"Oh, nothing," Jackie said as she patted the telescope tucked away in her back pocket. "I just needed a closer look, that's all!" ◉

Were your inferences correct? How do you find evidence as you read that supports your conclusions?

Up Close

Observe something in your classroom and jot down some sensory words that describe it. If you can, write words that refer to all the senses: sound, sight, touch, smell, and taste. Save your list to later write a poem about what you observed.

That's Not What I Thought!

Write a story about a time when something you inferred turned out to be incorrect. Discuss an incident in which an inference you made about someone or something you read, saw, or heard caused a problem of some kind. Explain how your inference led you to the wrong conclusion.

I Dare You

Have you ever accepted a dare or read about other characters accepting a dare? Write about what happened to you or the character you read about because a dare was accepted.

IS SEEING BELIEVING?

In the story "A Closer Look," Jackie sees something from her window that makes her think something awful has happened to her friend, Andrew. As it turns out, reality was different from what Jackie thought she saw.

Sometimes your eyes may play tricks on you. What do you see in these pictures? Are you sure? Look again! If you're mystified, ask your teacher for help.

1. Which blue circle is bigger?

2. Look at the blue box. Are the lines bent or straight?

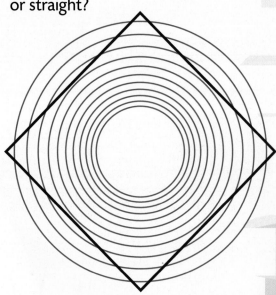

3. Are the black lines slanted or straight?

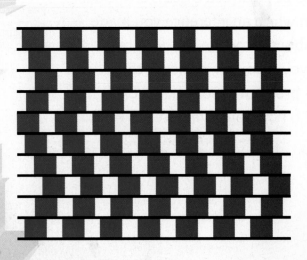

4. Do you see the yellow on the outside of the box or the inside?

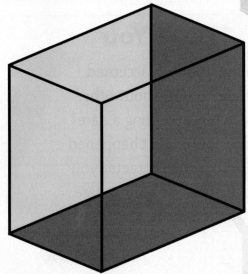

Meet Georgienne Bradley, Underwater Photographer

An Interview by Lisa Rao

How would **you** like a **job** swimming with **sharks** and **dolphins** all day? Let's visit with someone who **zooms in** on these and other ocean creatures . . .

Goergienne originally
wanted to be a doctor.
Now she works underwater!

When did you realize that you wanted to be an underwater photographer?

Well, it was not my first career choice. When I was in college, I had decided to pursue a career in medicine. But while I was in medical school, I received a surprising phone call from a friend needing some help with a photography assignment. He needed an excellent diver who could fluently speak Spanish because the job involved travel throughout Latin America. I speak Spanish and love to dive, so I fit the job. And that was the launch of a new career for me. I've never looked back since trying the work! Before helping my friend, I hadn't dreamed that the diving I loved to do for fun and as a hobby could be my life's work.

Sometimes we hear stories about people who were afraid of the ocean as children but then learned to love the sea. Were you ever afraid of the water?

I was never the least bit afraid of the water. However, this was actually a bad thing. I was so comfortable in the water that I did not have the proper respect for the power of the sea. I felt invincible, as if nothing would hurt or stop me in the water. This is really a very dangerous way to feel! A good diver is confident, but respects the sea and is always careful.

Why do you think it would be dangerous to feel invincible in the sea?

Do you have a favorite photograph?

I have many favorite photos. Most of these are of animals that are endangered. I hope people viewing my photographs will be moved to protect environments that are endangered throughout the world.

But do you enjoy taking pictures of a favorite sea creature?

More than any other creatures, I love taking photographs of sharks. These creatures are majestic and greatly misunderstood. I respect these predators, and I feel privileged when I get close enough to them to capture a good photograph.

What was your best experience as an underwater photographer?

Funny enough, my best experience and worst experience were the same one! I had a job to videotape a shark feeding frenzy for a television program, but it was getting toward the end of my trip and I hadn't seen any sharks! I was getting worried because I didn't want to disappoint the producers. During my last day on location, I was tired and ready to give up when I thought I saw a little activity on the water's surface. When our team reached the area, my partner, Jay, jumped into the water. He immediately surfaced and yelled, "This is it! Let's go!" I quickly scrambled into my gear and dove into a frenzy of feeding sharks, dolphin, tuna, diving birds, and other creatures. Small bait fish were frantically trying to escape the larger predatory animals. I was at once both absolutely terrified and ecstatic to be filming this phenomenal activity.

How many pictures do you usually take during an assignment?

I rarely return to the surface without shooting at least one full roll of film. There are 36 images per roll, and I sometimes carry up to three cameras. That means I can shoot up to 108 images on a dive that lasts only 40 minutes! This allows me to experiment with different lighting angles. All too often, I arrive back at the surface to find the friendliest turtle or dolphin waiting for me—a perfect photo opportunity—and I am totally out of film. These situations used to frustrate me. I had to wrestle with an important decision: Should I take fewer photos in the water and save some film just in case

Certain underwater life can be dangerous—like these hammerhead sharks.

I spot something beautiful on the surface? I decided against it. It would be impossible to predict if there would be something exciting out of the water. And you know, now I realize that even a perfect photograph cannot come close to the image in a special memory my mind carries. Photographic images are a mere snap and moment of an event, but I remember all the emotions that I felt. In memory, I recall the temperature of the water and the chill that went up my spine when a wild mother dolphin trusted me enough to allow her baby to approach and cuddle under my arm.

In your opinion, what makes a good photograph?

Wow! That's a tough question. There are so many things that can contribute to a good image. My topmost considerations:

- Is the subject rare?

- Is the subject facing the camera and showing an interesting expression?

- Are the conditions in the area around the subject (the background) clean and not distracting?

- Is the image colorful?

- Does the image capture a special moment between animals or an interesting activity, such as eating, fighting, bathing, or birthing?

Top: An example of the beautiful coral Georgienne has photographed.
Bottom: Georgienne with a dolphin.

- Does the subject appeal only to me, or would a large audience of people enjoy viewing this photograph?

Then, of course, there are also the basic technical photography questions, such as, is the picture too light or too dark, or is the image blurry? When all of these elements, or parts, are considered, I can better judge the photograph's worth.

Did you take school courses that helped you learn your work?

I took many biology courses. Remember, I thought I was going into medicine! Photography and videography have been self-taught. I wish I had the opportunity to study this art in school, but I haven't found the time for it. I read as much as possible and learn on the job. However, it's been important that while I was in school, I really tried to study and learn well. That opened the door for many "cool" opportunities as I got older.

What are you most proud of in your work?

My photography work shows the beauty that lies in the ocean. If humankind can relate to this undersea world, they will be more likely to try to protect it. I dedicate my work to helping save endangered animals and their environments.

What advice would you give to kids who would like to be underwater photographers?

Study, ask lots of questions, and most of all, never let anyone tell you that you can't reach your dream. ◉

Based on what you read in Georgienne Bradley's interview, would you like to be an underwater photographer? Why or why not?

"If *humankind* can *relate* to this **undersea** world, they will be *more* likely to try to **protect** it."

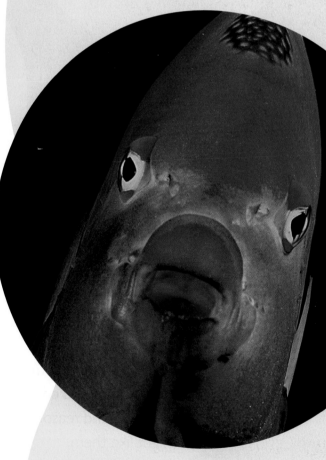

Georgienne got up close and personal with this angelfish.

Underwater

Imagine diving with Georgienne Bradley. How might you work together? What might you see? What might happen? Write a short paragraph describing your imaginary underwater dive.

Scary Sea Creatures

Draw a picture of the sea creature you'd *least* like to meet on an underwater photography assignment. Explain your choice to someone.

What Makes a Great Photograph?

In the interview, Georgienne Bradley talks about what she thinks makes a great photograph. Think about what Georgienne believes are a good photograph's strong points. Find some examples that you think would fit her list. Get together with several classmates and compare photographs and reasons people might like them.

Close Calls!

What do these photographs show? (Here's a hint: they're all close-up views of common, everyday objects.) Make your best guesses, and then check with your teacher for the correct answers.

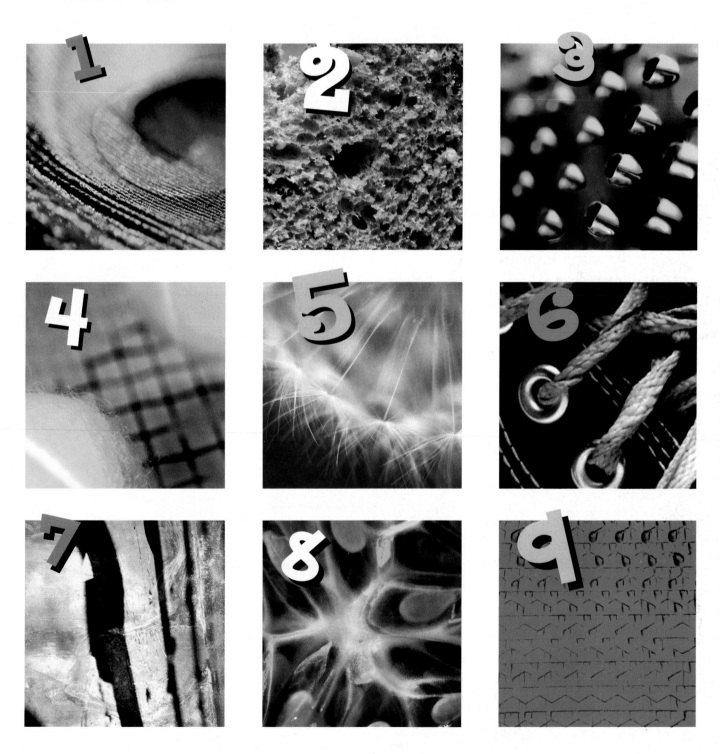

INFERRING

Alevia Saves Borglene!

Charlie and Sam have finished reading their book. They thought back to the many other science-fiction books they had read together and agreed that this one was one of the best ever.

"Your prediction was right," Charlie said to Sam. "Alevia turned out to be really brave. Her planet would have been destroyed if she hadn't been able to get the secret formula back!"

"That's true," said Sam. "But your inference about Alevia made sense, too. She couldn't have saved her planet if she hadn't learned to stand up for what she believed in. I changed one of my predictions, too. At first I thought the Whamulins were going to help her find the formula. But they turned out to be her enemies. What a great book! I hope there'll be a sequel."

Think about a time in your reading when you expected something to happen that didn't. Did you then make another prediction about what would happen? Careful readers make **inferences** and change their predictions as they read, almost without knowing they do it. To make these inferences, they use what they know from other reading, television shows, conversations with friends, and many other experiences.

In the next story, you'll be zooming with Maggie and Hank into an experience that is, well . . . out of this world!

Once and for All

by M. C. Hall

"It's your fault!" cried Maggie.

"It is not!" replied Hank, snapping his bubble gum.

Maggie gave her twin brother a dirty look. Then she studied the boxes and stacks of old magazines lying everywhere around them. It would take all day to clean the shed. But they had to do it. "I'm tired of arguments about who's best at what," Mom had said. "Go clean the shed—and figure out who's the best worker!"

Now, an hour later, the twins had barely touched the mess. Maggie sighed and reached for a dusty box. She almost missed the clink as something hit the floor.

"Oh, it's a whistle," Maggie said, picking it up.

"Give it to me!" Hank demanded.

"No! I found it!" Maggie lifted the whistle to her lips, closed her eyes, and blew. Not even a tiny peep came from the whistle. Disgusted, she opened her eyes.

Hank looked strange. His lips were moving, but words weren't coming out. Expecting a trick, Maggie asked, "What's wrong with you?"

"L-L-Look," stammered Hank.

Maggie's eyes widened. They were no longer in the shed. They were at the edge of a huge sports playing field. Massive wooden stands stood empty along the sidelines. "Where are we?" she asked in a whisper.

"I don't know," replied Hank. "The shed . . . well, it dissolved."

"That's impossible!" cried Maggie, staring at the whistle.

"It did dissolve!" retorted Hank. "And now—"

A voice startled them. "You're here!"

Maggie stuffed the whistle into her pocket. A short, chubby man had come into view. His round head was bald except for a fringe of hair over each ear.

"What—" began Hank.

"There's no time," interrupted the little man. "Follow me."

Maggie grabbed his arm. "Wait! Who are you? And where are we?"

"Who am I? Why, I'm Crumb, Master of the Games."

"Games?" echoed Maggie. "What games?"

"The Once-and-for-All Games," said Crumb. "That's why you're here. To settle things once and for all."

"What?" asked Hank again.

Crumb pulled out a notebook. Quickly, he turned pages. "Yes, yes," he muttered. "Here it is—Maggie and Hank Jenson, arguing all the time about who's fastest, strongest, and smartest." He looked up with a satisfied expression. "I'm rarely wrong. Now, wait here—and don't bother trying to whistle your way out of here. The whistle won't work until we have a champion." Then he trotted off.

What do you think is happening to Maggie and Hank? Why do you think so?

A moment later, a woman appeared at their side. She, too, was short and round. A cloud of curly red hair framed an attractive face.

"Welcome," the woman said. "I'm Midge, your supervisor." Her bright eyes inspected Maggie and Hank. "You'll do," she said at last. "Come this way, please."

She led the twins toward a door set into the stands, a door that Maggie realized she hadn't seen earlier. They entered a huge locker room. "We don't have long," said Midge, "so sit down."

Numbly, Maggie and Hank sank to a bench. All was silent as Midge thumbed through a thin booklet. "You'll start with— no, that's wrong. Let's see . . . Ah yes, Noggin Ball," she said. "The rules are—" A bell clanged. "Oh my, there's no more time!" cried Midge. "Let's go!" She shooed the twins out the door and onto the field. A great cheer greeted them. Thousands of short, plump spectators now sat in the stands.

"Who are *they?*" asked Maggie.

"They're your fans, here to cheer you," responded Midge. "Now, hurry. Crumb is ready to judge the events."

A tall chair stood in the middle of the field. Perched on the top of it was Crumb. He raised a megaphone to his lips and the cheering stopped.

"Welcome to the Once-and-for-All Games," Crumb announced, "where Maggie and Hank Jenson will test who is best!"

Crumb addressed the twins. "Remember, in Noggin Ball, you must move the ball with your head. Are you ready? Begin!"

Hank was in motion immediately. Crawling on his hands and knees, he pushed a lopsided ball with his head. Spotting another ball at her feet, Maggie started after him. It was too late. Hank beat her to the finish line by a minute.

Maggie's fans groaned, but Hank's went wild, shouting "Hank! Hank!"

"My ball is defective," Maggie muttered.

"There's nothing wrong with it," hissed Hank. "I'm just faster."

Crumb was announcing the next event. "And now, the Reverse Climb!" Six men carried a huge stepladder onto the field. It looked ordinary, except for having rungs on both sides. "You'll climb backward up one side and down the other," stated Crumb.

Maggie won the event, despite the fact that the rungs stretched like rubber. But Hank won Hedge Bowling. His spiny green ball bounced down the edge of the field, through a hedge, and into a hole. Maggie's ball got hung up in the branches.

Next, Maggie won the Thumb Run. Hank couldn't keep his balance with his thumbs tied together behind his back.

"The morning games are over," Crumb announced. Both sides cheered wildly until a signal from Crumb silenced them. "Be back at one o'clock for Jellyball," he told everyone.

As the crowd made excited noises, Maggie and Hank looked at each other. Jellyball?

Have you confirmed or changed your earlier inference? What information in the text did you use to do this?

"It's lunchtime," called Midge. She hurried the twins through the locker room door. Inside, a table was set for them. "Enjoy yourselves," said Midge. "After all, it's your last meal together."

"What?" cried Maggie.

"Huh?" mumbled Hank.

"Oh, yes. We only got halfway through the rule book, didn't we? Well, the loser returns to your world. The champion stays here."

"Then I don't want to win!" cried Maggie.

"Me neither!" shouted Hank.

"That's nonsense. Of course you do. There's plenty of evidence. You both *always* want to win. That's why you're here." With that, Midge left.

"I'm having a nightmare," said Maggie.

"I am, too," sighed Hank.

"It's *my* dream," Maggie countered.

"No, it's not!"

"Yes, it—" Maggie stopped. "We can't argue now, Hank. We've got to figure out what to do."

"Let's run for it," suggested Hank.

"Run? Unless you've seen a door marked 'This way to reality,' there's no place to run," replied Maggie.

Hank's forehead creased in thought. Suddenly looking brighter, he said "OK, let's *both* lose."

"Oh, that's a creative idea!" snorted Maggie. "We don't even know what Jellyball is. Besides, someone *has* to win!"

They fell silent. Finally, Maggie asked, "Where's the rule book?" A mad search led them to the bench where Midge had left it.

They started reading. "Oh great!" said Hank at last. "We throw wiggly balls at invisible targets. How can we be sure to miss?"

"Keep reading," said Maggie.

Twenty minutes later, she sighed. "At least we know we can get home by blowing the whistle."

"Yeah," said Hank. "But it won't take the champion back." He popped a stick of gum into his mouth and soon blew a very sticky bubble.

"Hank," said Maggie slowly as she watched him, "I have an idea."

> What do you think Maggie's idea is? What clues in the text led you to this conclusion?

"It's time to go," said Midge, hurrying into the room. Cheers again greeted them as they walked out onto the field.

Midge handed out the jellyballs, which quivered like gelatin and felt like it, too. Then Crumb explained the rules. "A dozen targets are set up nearby," he said, pointing down the field. "They're invisible until hit. The first player to hit one wins. Are you ready? Begin."

Maggie clutched her jellyball in one hand. She stretched her arm back and over her head, and then she hurled it forward.

The jellyball shook, stretched slightly, and then only plopped at Maggie's feet. "Oh-h-h . . . ," sighed her fans.

The same thing happened to Hank. The crowd started booing. "Midge," shouted Crumb, "check the jellyballs!"

Midge rolled her eyes. "I have to do everything," she muttered. She picked up one quivery ball and then another. "They're fine."

"They aren't fine," insisted Maggie.

"You try, Midge," suggested Hank.

Midge wound up. Then she let go. Her jellyball flew down the field. *Smack!* A shimmering target appeared as the ball stuck in an outside ring.

"That decides the championship! Midge is the champion!" cried Maggie.

"Hooray!" yelled Hank.

As a low rumble ran through the crowd, Crumb shouted, "No! She can't be!"

"Yes, she can," said Hank respectfully. "Look closely at page 34 of the rule book. Jellyball is only played when there's a tie, and the winner is the champion of the games—always!"

"Congratulations, Midge!" shouted Maggie. She pulled the whistle from her pocket and raised it to her lips.

"We're home!" cried Maggie.

"Thanks to you," said Hank. "You had a great idea!"

"It wouldn't have worked without your gum," said Maggie generously. "And that reminds me—my fingers are still sticky."

"Mine are too," said Hank. "But the gum kept those jellyballs from going anywhere."

Maggie added, "We were also lucky that Midge hit a target."

"I would've made her keep demonstrating until she did," laughed Hank.

Maggie looked at the whistle in her hand and then at the garbage can against the wall. "Well, what do you think?" At Hank's nod, Maggie tossed the whistle into the trash. "Now, let's get right to work cleaning up this mess," she said.

"You'll get no argument from me," Hank said with a laugh. ◯

> Was your inference correct? If not, reread page D22 to look for any clues you might have missed.

Stop and Respond

Getting Along

Maggie and Hank are twins who argue, as brothers and sisters sometimes do. What do brothers and sisters argue about? Talk with a classmate about creative ways brothers and sisters can solve squabbles. Then work together to make a cartoon showing how a brother and sister solved a problem. Don't forget to use speech balloons to show what your characters said!

To Compete or Not to Compete

Do you enjoy competition? Do you think it brings out the best in people? Write about what's good and not so good about competition. Do you think there is too much, just the right amount, or not enough of it?

Invent a Game

Maggie and Hank compete in some pretty wacky events at the Once-and-for-All Games, including Noggin Ball, Reverse Climb, Thumb Run, and Jellyball. Invent another "off-the-wall" game. Think of a funny name for the game and write a brief description of how it is played. Who would be the winner of your game?

Game Kids

by Linda Johns

"Go faster than you ever imagined!" flashed a banner on the computer screen.

"Wow! Just think how far I could go if I could just get my robo-jet to go faster and climb higher in this game," said Jamie.

She clicked on the banner.

"Get to Level 78 with this Simple Game Tips Kit!" exclaimed the next page of the ad. Of course, she would need to pay $19.95 if she wanted any game tips sent straight to her.

The truth is that Jamie is getting better at the computer game every time she plays it. She doesn't need to pay anything—especially not $19.95—for game tips. Sure, she's run into her share of walls and fallen through some dark holes. She's even had to start completely over from Level 1 when her younger brother erased the game from the hard drive. But each week she gets to a higher level.

Maybe, like Jamie, you're getting so good at playing a computer game that you think it will soon start to get dull. What's a game girl or boy to do when this happens? Make a game of your own!

Who Makes Games?

Do you ever wonder who makes computer games today? The answer may surprise you—kids just like you! Yes, more and more kids are creating their own games. If you have the tools and the time, you too can create games, design Web pages, and even make robots.

At some cybercamps, kids between the ages of seven and sixteen can spend an entire week working with computer whizzes. Campers learn the steps of making a game and how to do their own programming. However, it is possible for you to create your own computer games without going to a special camp. But how do you start?

Getting Started

A tiny computer circuit, called a microchip, is the technological key of computer and video games. A microchip acts like a memory. It tells the computer what to do to keep a game moving. It keeps track of each player's moves and saves the score. But you don't really have to know exactly how or why it works. It's more important to know what makes a game challenging and fun for players.

Think about the computer games you know. Have you noticed that in the majority of games a character is guided along a journey? The journey might take you through a castle 400 years ago. It might be putting a rock band together. Or the journey might be to win a game show. The player's job is usually to guide a character through the journey, whatever it is.

You might take a tip from professionals who design games for a living. They break the game-making process into five steps. If any step is skipped, a game just won't work.

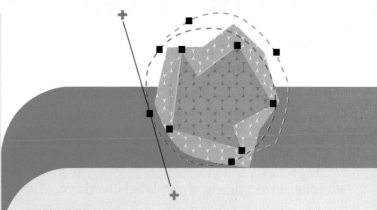

Work Up Your Story

Although you don't have to be a technology wizard to make a good computer game, you do have to be a good storyteller. As a first step, think about the four *w's*. These are *who, what, where,* and *when*.

The *who* will be your characters. Make them interesting. Give them original names. Be goofy, sinister, or spooky as you have fun imagining them!

The *what* is your plot. Decide if you want an adventure game, a racing game, or a test of knowledge. Then think of something to keep your game moving along. A good plot can usually be boiled down to this simple formula: Someone wants something that someone else has. Your main character may want the key to the golden treasure chest, but someone else has it. Or your main character might already have the key to the golden treasure chest, but a three-headed monster wants it.

The *where* and *when* will be your setting. Is your story set under the ocean? on top of a lonely mountain? in outer space? And will this journey be happening in the present, during the past, or in the future?

Design Your Visuals

Your game needs to look attractive. When it does, it will be described as having *good visuals*.

You can start visual designing by developing your characters. How do you want them to look? You might sketch them on paper. Or you can draw them on your computer with a drawing program. As you draw, think as you did when you first imagined your characters. Are they wacky, funny, or scary? How can you best show that? Use your imagination!

Three-dimensional (3D) graphics include characters and objects that look rounded and stand out from whatever is behind them. In real life, most people see everything around them as three-dimensional. But most computer games have characters and objects that look flat. This makes it a lot easier to make a game because you can finish your characters with a drawing program and later, in another step, make them move.

Good visuals also mean making sure words and instructions are easy to see and read. And don't forget to be inventive with patterns on clothing or objects and with backgrounds.

Based on your own experiences with computer games and the information in the text, what kind of characters do you think kids would like?

Create Storyboards

The next step is to draw your story as a set of storyboards. These are like cartoon squares that will show the basic action of your game from the beginning to the end. Keep your storyboards simple, making quick sketches and adding short labels to them.

Many professional game designers make storyboards. Some put pen to paper and sketch out their ideas. Others use computer software to show different scenes. Making storyboards either way helps you to set the basic framework of your game.

Now you have your characters and your basic story. It's time to get things moving!

Add Action

You don't need any special knowledge to add movement to your game. Animation computer programs do the work for you. In fact, you can use computer characters that are already animated. Or you can follow simple directions to get your characters to make all the moves you want.

Game designers talk a lot about a game's *interface*. This involves how people will physically act to play the game and join in its action. Take some advice from the pros and keep things as simple as possible. Buttons should be very visible and easy to get to. A player might use arrow keys to move around in game screens or click on buttons to choose answers.

Now you're ready to put it all together!

Program the Game

Programming, making the coded instructions which a computer needs to run your game, is the step that may seem the trickiest. The good news is that you do not always have to do this step by yourself. You can still have a great computer game, even if you do not program. There are Web sites that let you choose your characters and your story. You make choices about how the game looks or works, but you don't need to have the technical knowledge because someone has already done the programming.

Game creators use computer programming languages such as Java and C++. If you're interested, you can learn how to create in these languages. Some people think it must be very complicated and difficult. But the truth is that if you can write and do math, you can program a computer. Really!

> Based on what you have read, do you think you would be good at designing computer games? Why or why not?

Most companies creating computer games spend a lot of money for game design and marketing. Because there are many of these businesses, most of them are looking to hire smart, creative new game designers to help them make and sell great new games. People at today's top computer companies know that the best game-makers of the future are probably the kids who are playing games today. And it's no surprise to them that kids like you are also already designing them!

Name the Game

Computer game titles are really important because people reading the title will quickly infer something about the game. Even if you invented the most exciting computer game in the world, it might not sell without the right title. Computer games must have great titles to get players to want to play them for the first time. Try your hand at making up game names. Make a list of at least five exciting titles. Try them out on a friend. Which title does he or she like best?

The Best!

Get together with a small group of classmates and discuss the computer games you like. Then write a description of your favorite computer game, explain why it is your favorite, and try to persuade readers that it's the best computer game ever.

Take Sides

Do you think your friends spend too much time playing computer games? Would their time be better spent on other activities? Or are computer games a great way to develop eye and hand coordination, reasoning skills, and problem-solving abilities? Hold a debate with classmates on the value of computer games.

Let's Write

It Depends on How You Look at It

Choose an object around you and write two descriptions of it. For one, pretend to be over 100 feet tall, and for the second, pretend you are the size of an ant. How does the object look from each point of view?

It's the Little Things That Count

Observe something on your way to or from school—a plant or an animal—over a period of a week or so. Each day, look at the plant or animal carefully for a few minutes and write in a journal what you see, noting any changes, no matter how small. After a week of observation, write a sentence or two that summarizes the changes you noticed.

Watch Out!

Write a short story in which careful observation—or the lack of it—plays an important part. Your story could be a mystery with a detective who follows clues, an adventure in which scientists' careful observations lead to a great discovery, or a funny story about kids who thought they saw something they really didn't see.

More Books

Almond, David. *Skellig*. Delacorte, 1999.

Avi. *Nothing but the Truth: A Documentary Novel*. Jackson/Orchard, 1991.

Curtis, Christopher Paul. *Bud, Not Buddy*. Delacorte, 1999.

Dorris, Michael. *Sees Behind Trees*. Hyperion, 1996.

Edwards, Frank B. and Laurel Azíz. *Close Up: Microscopic Photographs of Everyday Stuff*. Bungaloo, 1992.

On the Web

Bits of History
http://members.aol.com/ccpaquin/

Bugscope's Images
http://bugscope.beckman.uiuc.edu/
gallery/gallery.htm

Exploratorium Online Exhibits
http://www.exploratorium.edu/
exhibits/f_exhibits.html

Rose's Animated Gifs
http://www.wanderers2.com/rose/
animate.html

Across the Curriculum

Drama

Many people think Galileo Galilei, an Italian astronomer, discovered the telescope, but the telescope was actually invented by Hans Lippershey, a spectacle (eyeglasses) maker from the Netherlands. Do research about both men to discover their actual contributions to the development of the telescope. Then get together with a classmate and write a short skit that dramatizes Galileo and Lippershey meeting and discussing (and maybe even arguing!) about who should be honored as Inventor of the Year. Be creative—combine facts with drama and humor as you develop your skit.

Focus Power

A haiku is a short, three-line poem that "zooms in"—usually to focus on an aspect of nature. There are only 17 total syllables in the haiku; the first and third lines contain five syllables each, the second line contains seven. Matsuo Basho, a Zen monk who lived 400 years ago, is considered the master of haiku. He traveled across Japan teaching poetry and writing more than 1,000 haiki (the plural of haiku). Basho took his name from the wide-leafed banana tree (the basho tree), a present from a student, that shaded his house. Here are some haiki similar to the ones Basho wrote:

A calm hidden lake,
A frog leaps into the lake.
Plop! Splish! Calm no more.

The shiny white moon
throws quiet shadowy shapes
on the dark woods path.

Bright lazy morning,
We rub the night from our eyes.
My cat knows me well.

Would you like to try writing a haiku? Don't forget the syllable count: 5-7-5.